GRADE 1

Practice Book

A

The McGraw·Hill Companies

Macmillan/McGraw-Hill

Published by Macmillan/McGraw-Hill, of McGraw-Hill Education, a division of The McGraw-Hill Companies, Inc., Two Penn Plaza, New York, New York 10121.

Printed in the United States of America

5 6 7 8 HES 12 11 10

Contents

About this Book

The pages in the Practice Book provide practice for skills and concepts taught in the program. At the start of the grade, children will need support to complete the pages. As children progress through the grade, they will be more able to complete the pages independently.

Start Smart

Activities in the Start Smart section are to be completed with assistance from the teacher. These pages are **"Read Together"** pages: pages you read to children and assist them to complete.

Units 1-3

Continue to read the direction lines to children and to model how to complete the activities. Depending on the individual children, the following pages may be done independently by children working alone or in pairs.

- Phonics
- High-Frequency Words/Vocabulary
- Fluency
- Structural Analysis

The following pages are **Read Together**:

- Concepts of Print
- Oral Vocabulary and Read Aloud/ Listening Comprehension
- Text Features
- Literary Elements

Units 4-6

The **Read Together** pages in this part of the book are the Read Aloud/Listening Comprehension activities.

Start Smart

Contents

Unit 1 • All About Us

Contents

Unit 2 • Our Families, Our Neighbors

Contents

Unit 3 • Have Fun!

Contents

Unit 4 • Let's Team Up

Contents

Unit 5 • Nature Watch

Contents

Unit 6 • Adventures

Name ______________________

Say each picture name. Then write an **m** below the picture if its name begins like **map** or an **s** if its name begins like **sun**.

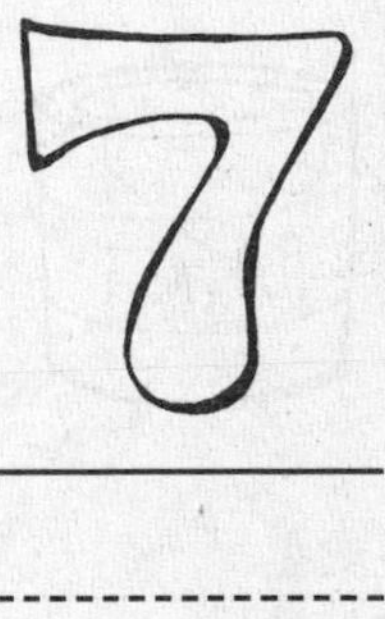

Write an **m** or **s** to complete the words.

____op 

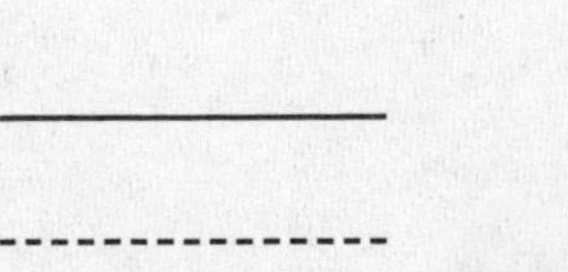

____ock 

TEKS **1.1 (A)** Recognize that spoken words are represented in written English by specific sequences of letters.
1.2 (E) Isolate initial sounds in one-syllable spoken words.

Name ______________________

Say each picture name. Then write a **p** below the picture if its name begins like **pin** or a **t** if its name begins like **turtle**.

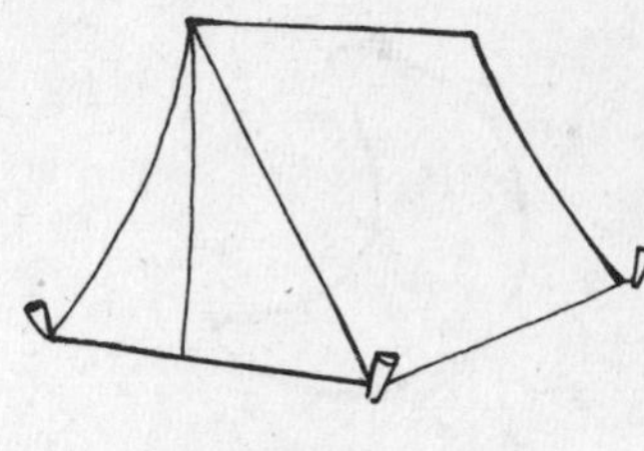

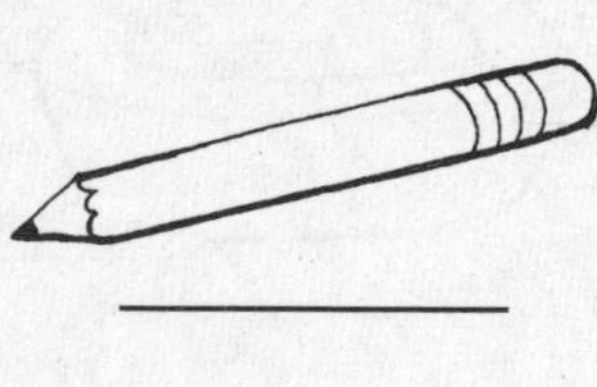

Write a **p** or **t** to complete the words.

____ig

____ent

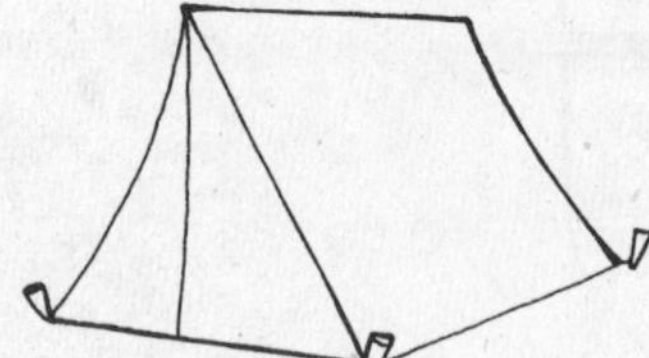

TEKS **1.1 (A)** Recognize that spoken words are represented in written English by specific sequences of letters.
1.2 (E) Isolate initial sounds in one-syllable spoken words.

High-Frequency Words:
like, can, the, I, we

4

1

TEKS **1.3 (H)** Identify and read at least 100 high-frequency words from a commonly used list.

TEKS **1.3 (H)** Identify and read at least 100 high-frequency words from a commonly used list.

Name ______________________

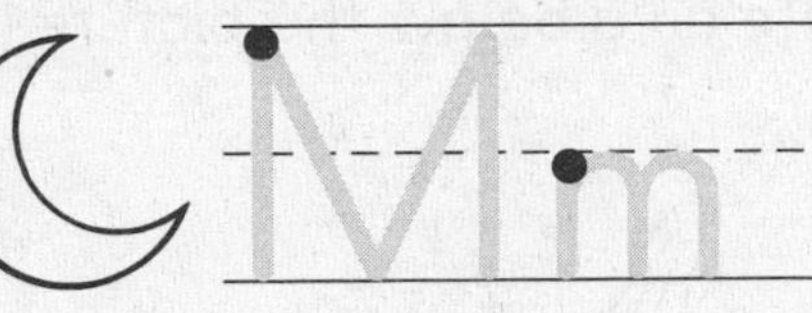

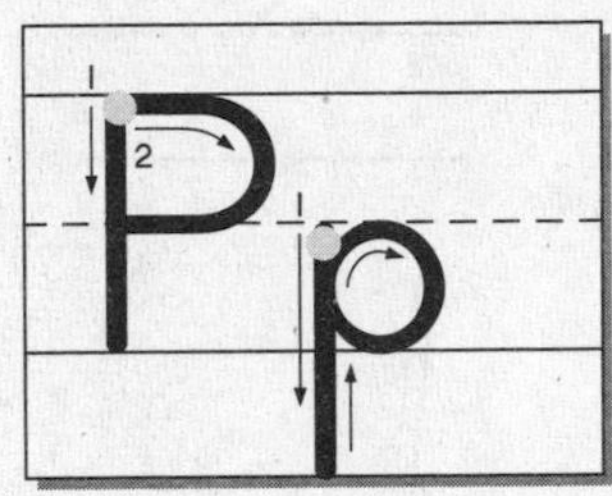

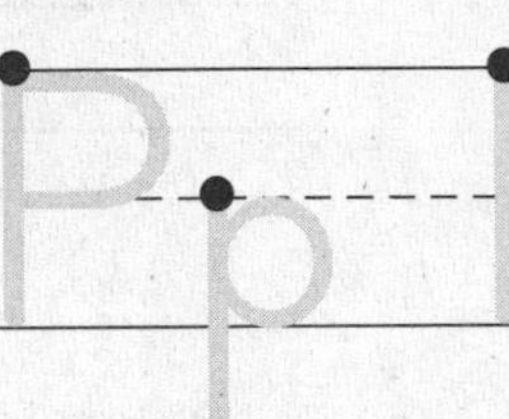
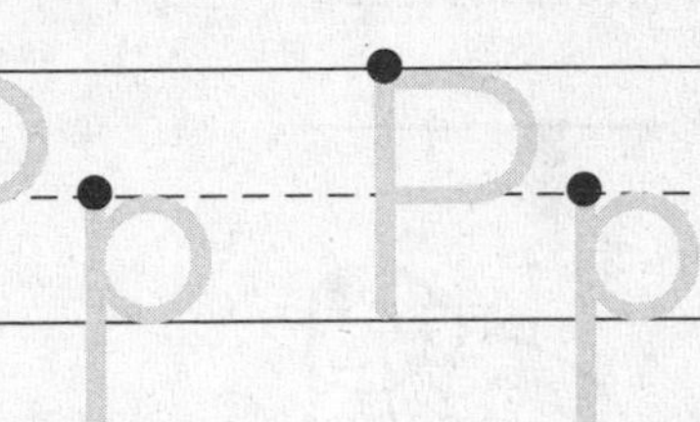

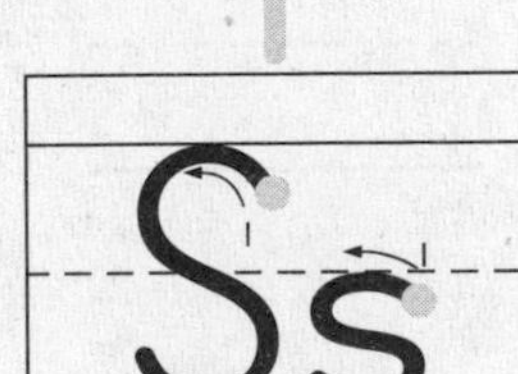

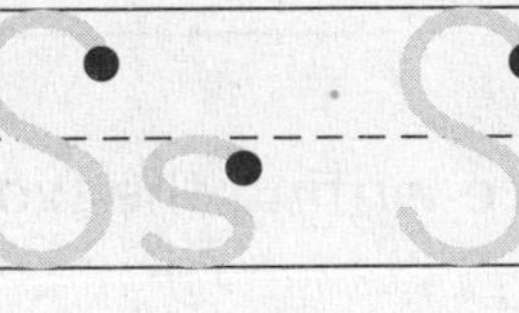
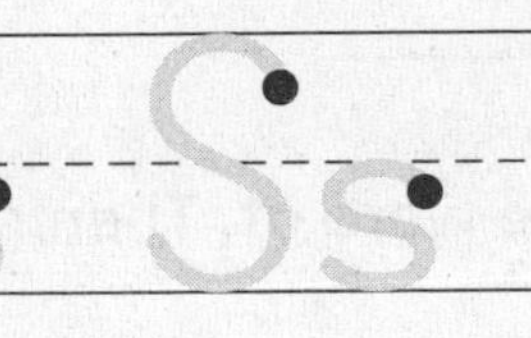

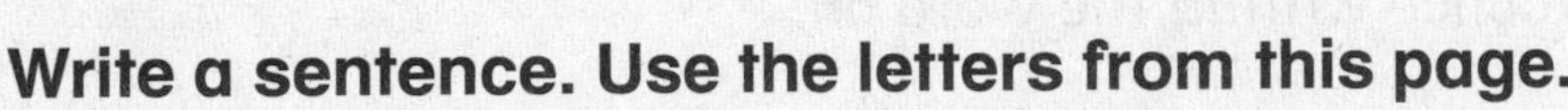

Write a sentence. Use the letters from this page.

TEKS **1.21 (A)** Form upper- and lower-case letters legibly in text, using the basic conventions of print, including spacing between words and sentences.

Name ___

Say each picture name. Then write an **a** below the picture if its name begins with **a** as in **apple**.

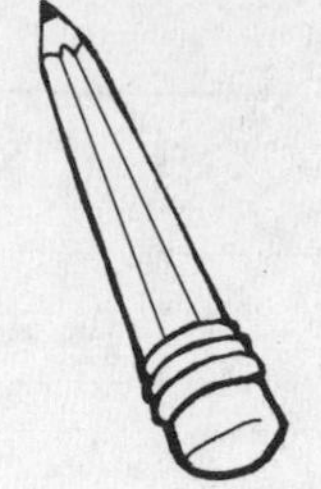

Trace the word **at**. Then practice writing the word **at**.

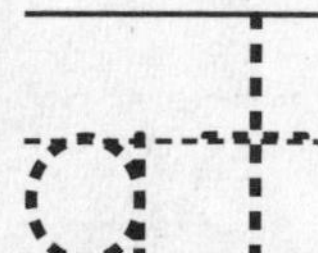

Trace the word **an**. Then practice writing the word **an**.

TEKS **1.1 (A)** Recognize that spoken words are represented in written English by specific sequences of letters.
1.2 (E) Isolate initial sounds in one-syllable spoken words.

Name ______________________

Say each picture name. Then write **c** below the picture if its name begins like **camel** or **n** if its name begins like **nest**.

Write an **a** to complete the words. Then read them.

c ___ t   m ___ n

c ___ n   m ___ p

TEKS **1.1 (A)** Recognize that spoken words are represented in written English by specific sequences of letters. **1.2 (D)** Blend spoken phonemes to form one-syllable words. **1.2 (E)** Isolate initial and medial sounds in one-syllable spoken words.

Practice

Handwriting: *Tt, Aa, Nn*

Name ________________________________

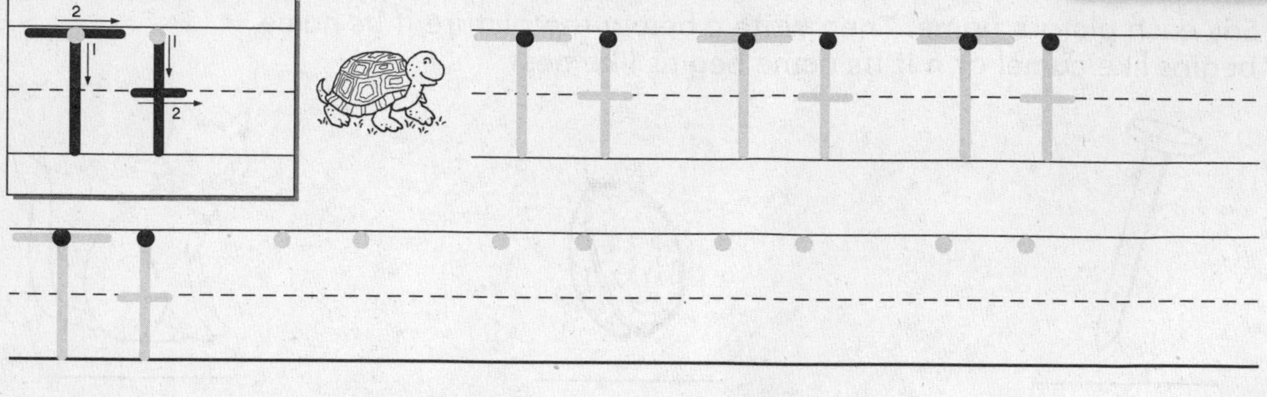

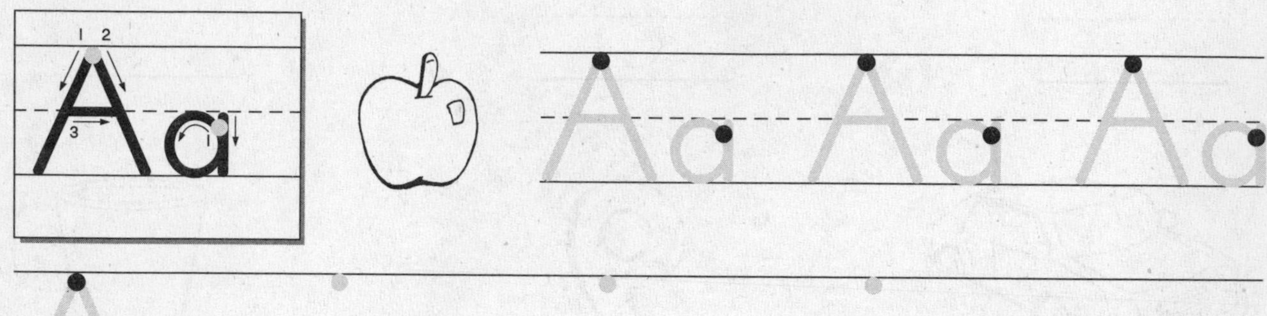

Write a sentence. Use the letters from this page.

TEKS **1.21 (A)** Form upper- and lower-case letters legibly in text, using the basic conventions of print, including spacing between words and sentences.

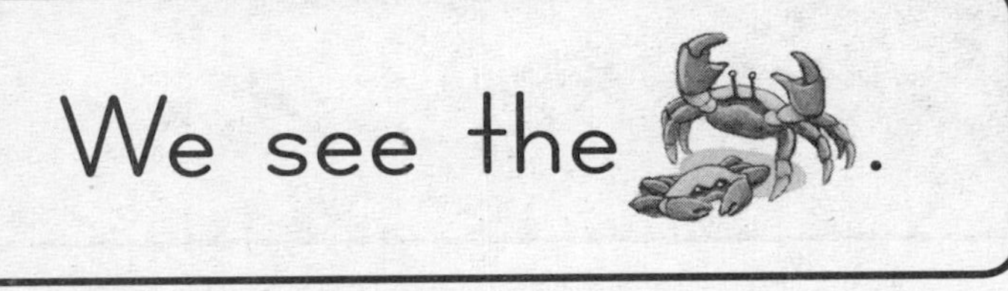

High-Frequency Words:
we, go, to, the, see

4

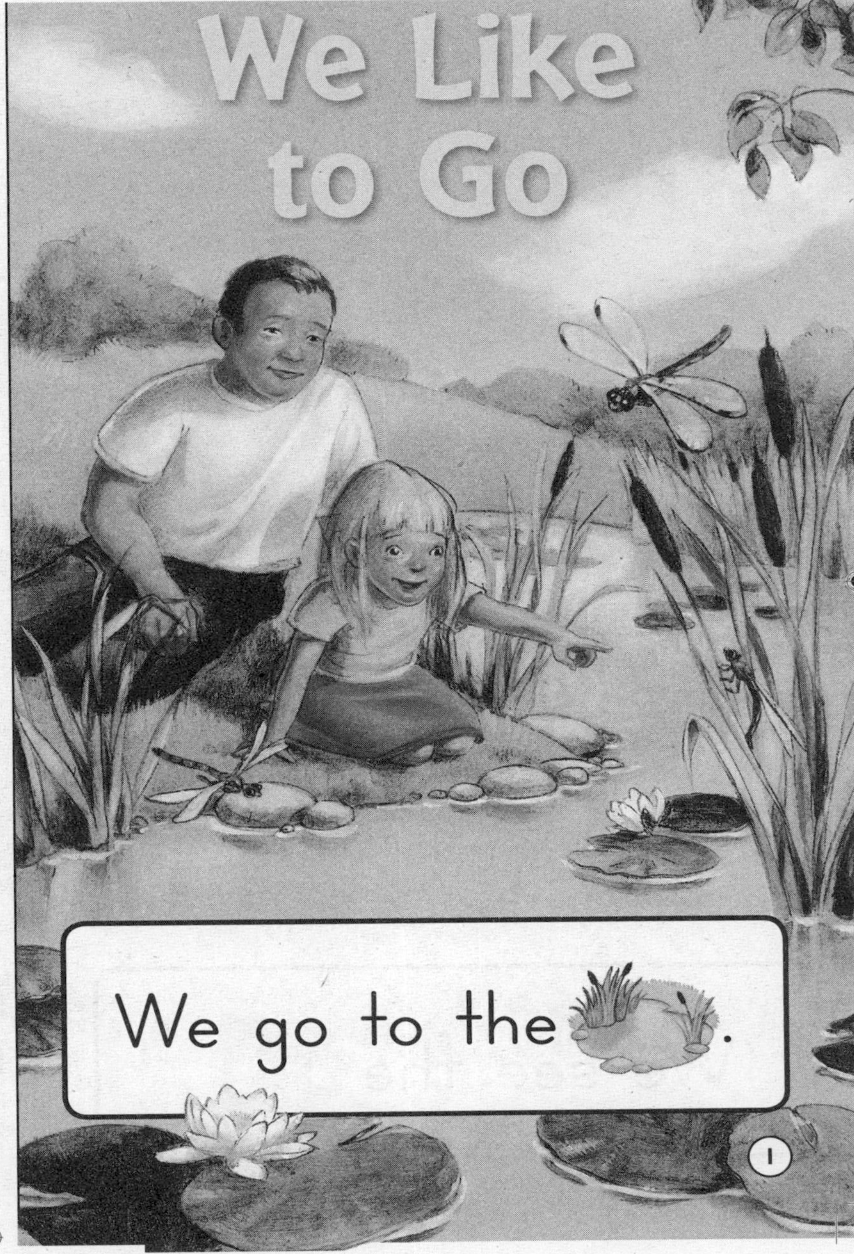

1

TEKS **1.3 (H)** Identify and read at least 100 high-frequency words from a commonly used list.

We see the 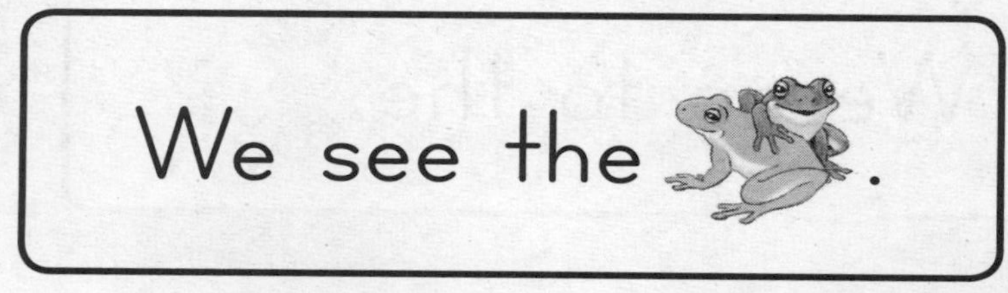.

2

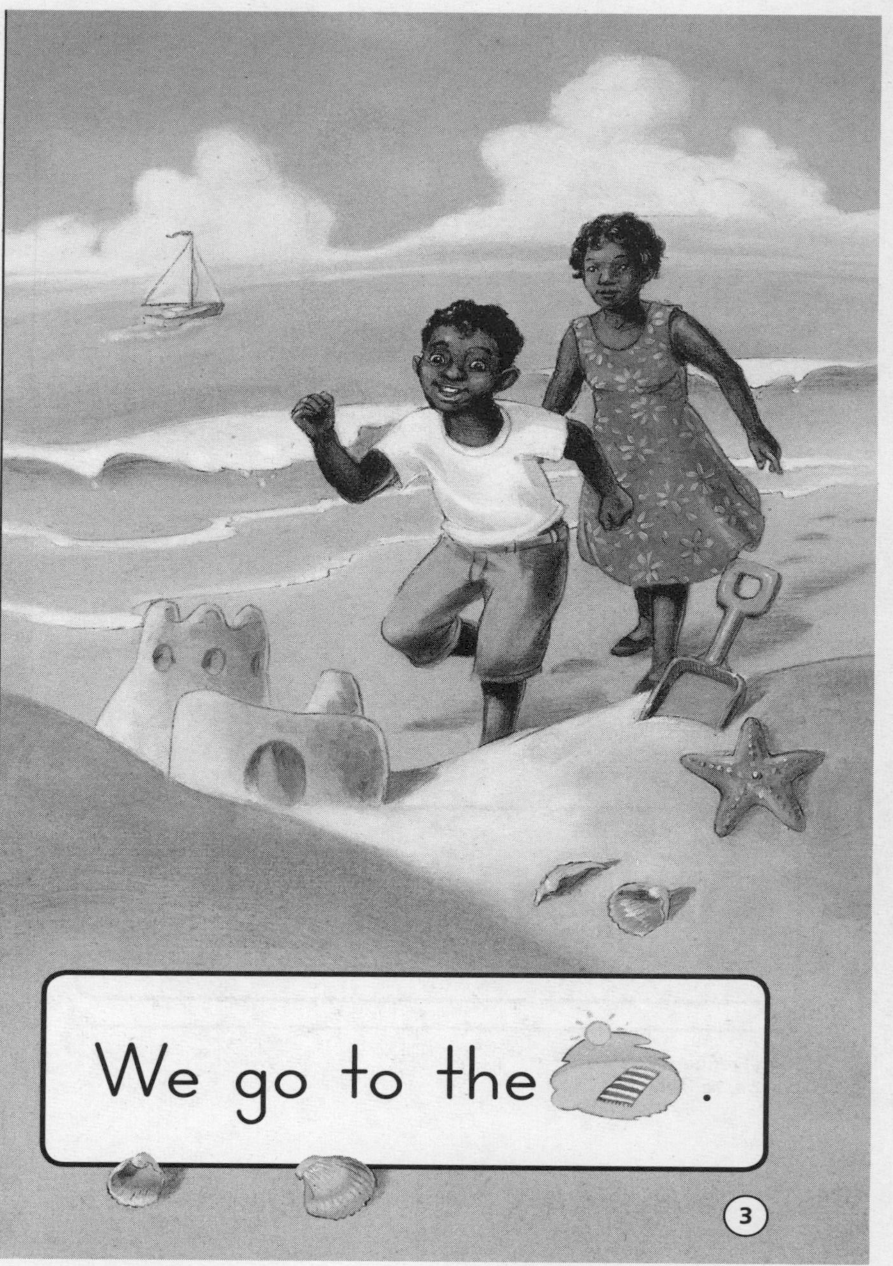

We go to the .

3

TEKS **1.3 (H)** Identify and read at least 100 high-frequency words from a commonly used list.

Name ______________________________

Say each picture name. Then write an **f** below the picture if its name begins like **fox** or an **h** if its name begins like **hat**.

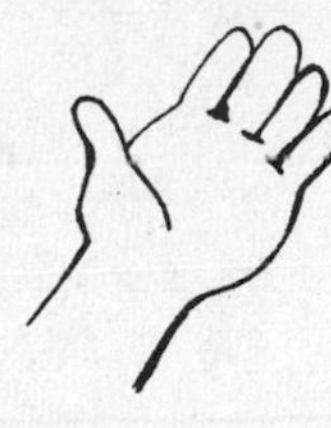

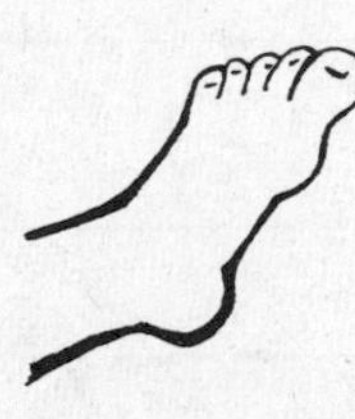

Trace the word **if**. Then practice writing the word **if**.

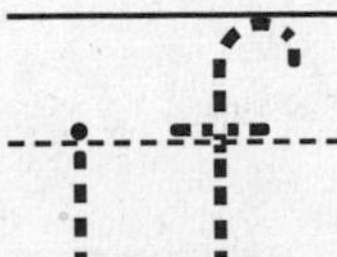

Write an **f** or **h** to complete the word.

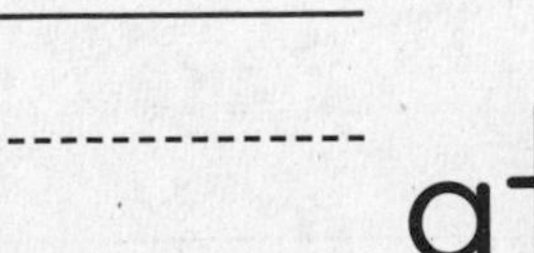

at

TEKS **1.1 (A)** Recognize that spoken words are represented in written English by specific sequences of letters.
1.2 (E) Isolate initial sounds in one-syllable spoken words.

Name ____________________

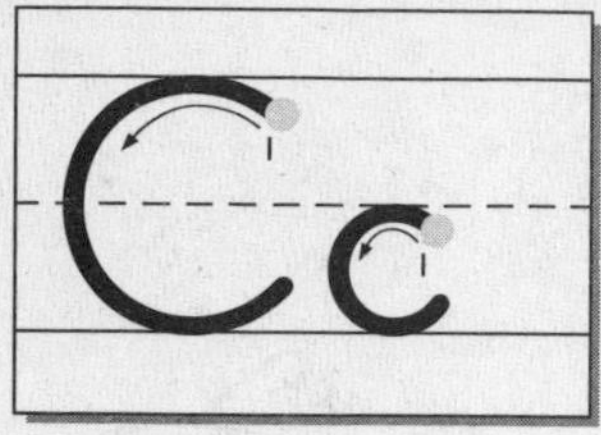

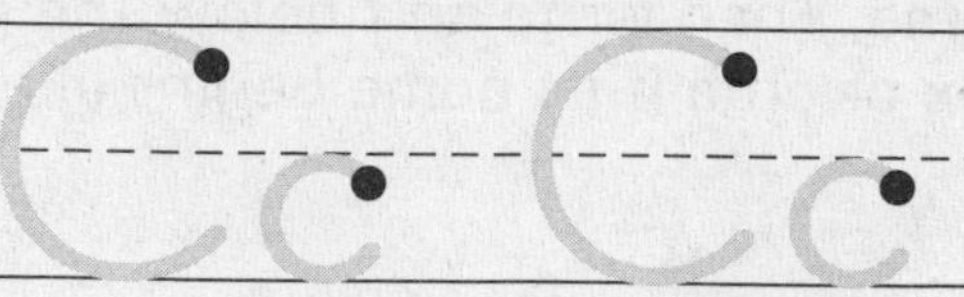

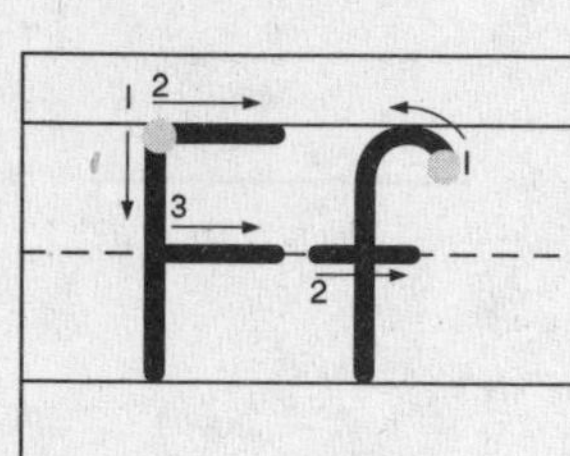

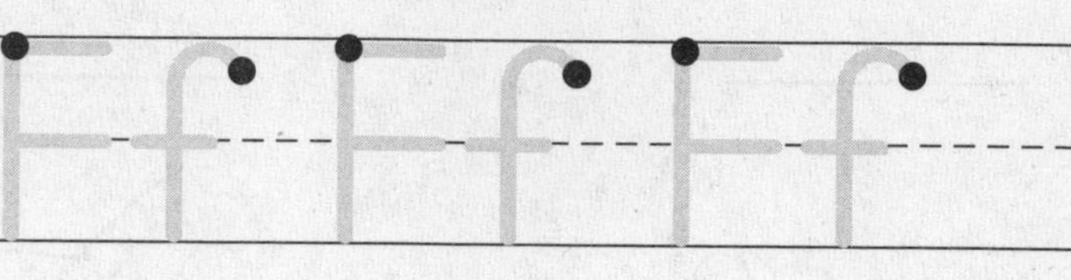

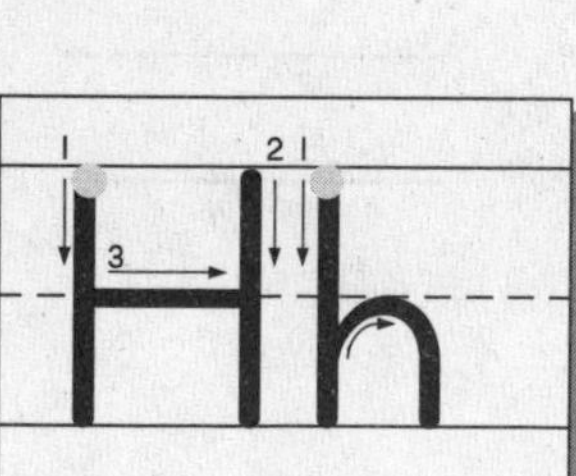

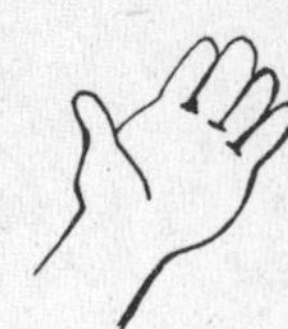

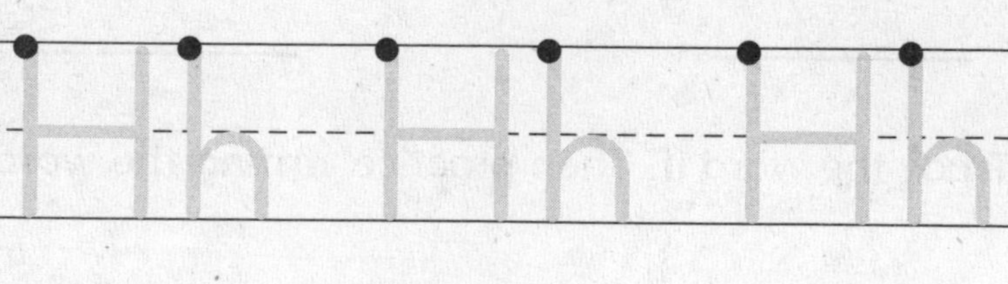

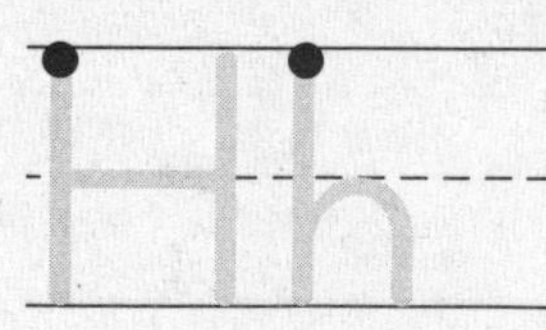

Write a sentence. Use the letters from this page.

TEKS **1.21 (A)** Form upper- and lower-case letters legibly in text, using the basic conventions of print, including spacing between words and sentences.

Name ____________________

Say each picture name. Then write an **i** below the picture if its name begins like **ink**.

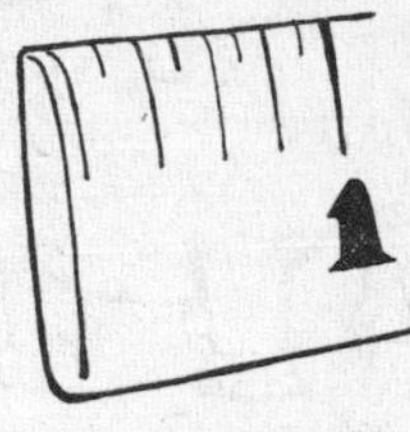

Trace the word **in**. Then practice writing the word **in**.

Trace the word **it**. Then practice writing the word **it**.

TEKS 1.1 (A) Recognize that spoken words are represented in written English by specific sequences of letters.
1.2 (E) Isolate initial sounds in one-syllable spoken words.

Name ______________________

Say each picture name. Then write a **d** below the picture if its name begins like **door** or an **r** if its name begins like **rose**.

Write **r** to complete the words. Then read the words.

____ at

____ an

Write **d** to complete the words. Then read the words.

____ ad

____ id

TEKS **1.1 (A)** Recognize that spoken words are represented in written English by specific sequences of letters. **1.2 (D)** Blend spoken phonemes to form one-syllable words. **1.2 (E)** Isolate initial sounds in one-syllable spoken words.

He is 

.

High-Frequency Words:
you, is, have

I have a .

TEKS **1.3 (H)** Identify and read at least 100 high-frequency words from a commonly used list.

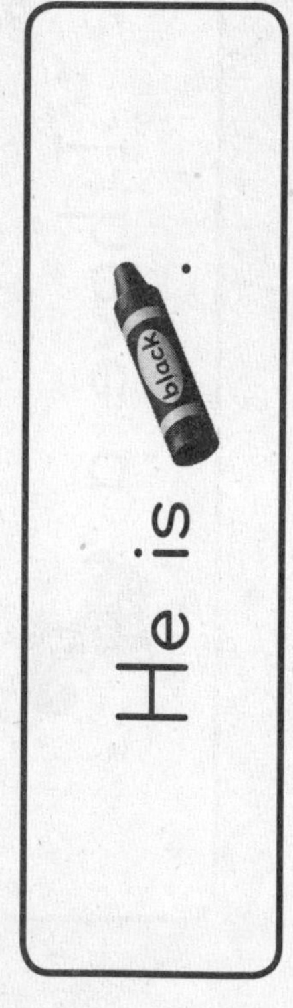

He is black.

2

You have a cat.

3

TEKS **1.3 (H)** Identify and read at least 100 high-frequency words from a commonly used list.

Name ______________________

Practice

Handwriting: ***Ii, Dd, Rr***

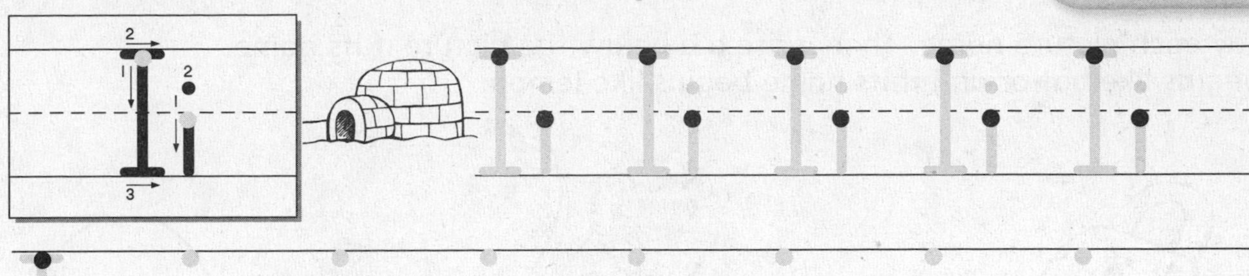

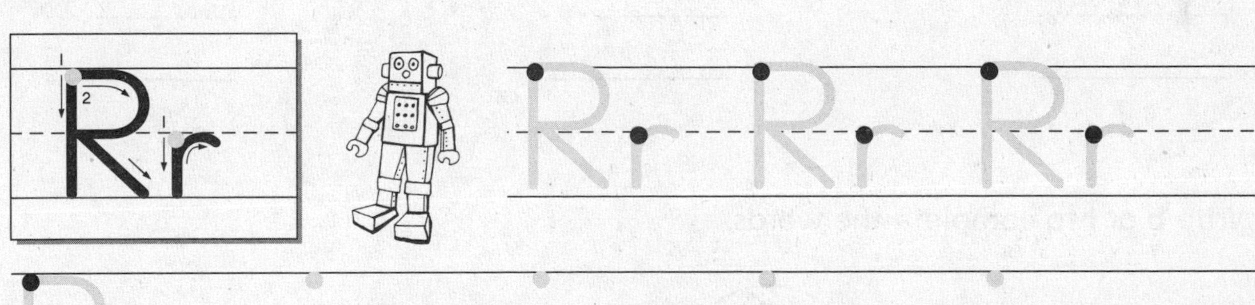

Write a sentence. Use the letters from this page.

TEKS **1.21 (A)** Form upper- and lower-case letters legibly in text, using the basic conventions of print, including spacing between words and sentences.

Name ________________

Say each picture name. Then write a **b** below the picture if its name begins like **bat** or an **l** if its name begins like **lemon**.

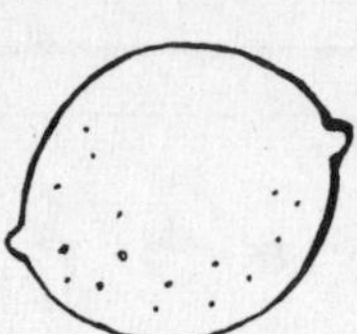

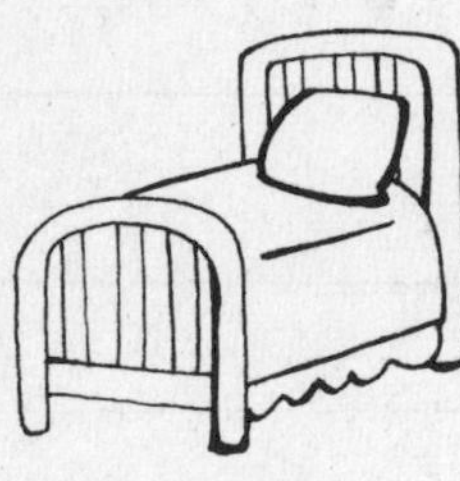

Write **b** or **l** to complete the words.

____ all

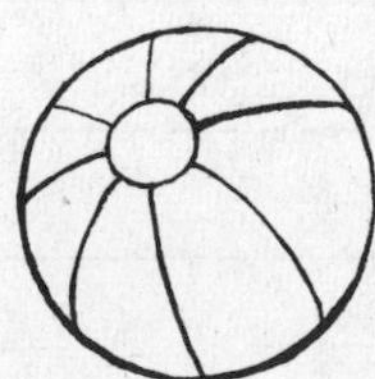

____ ips

TEKS **1.1 (A)** Recognize that spoken words are represented in written English by specific sequences of letters.
1.2 (E) Isolate initial sounds in one-syllable spoken words.

Name ______________________________

Say each picture name. Then write an **o** below the picture if its name begins like **ox**.

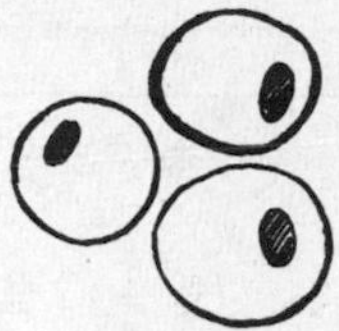

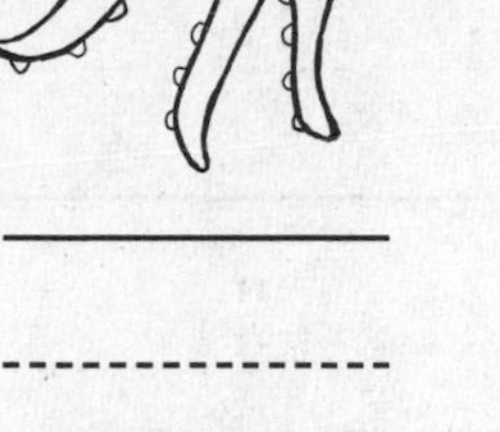

Trace the word **on**. Then practice writing the word **on**.

Write an **o** to complete the word.

___ x

TEKS **1.1 (A)** Recognize that spoken words are represented in written English by specific sequences of letters.
1.2 (E) Isolate initial sounds in one-syllable spoken words.

Name ____________________

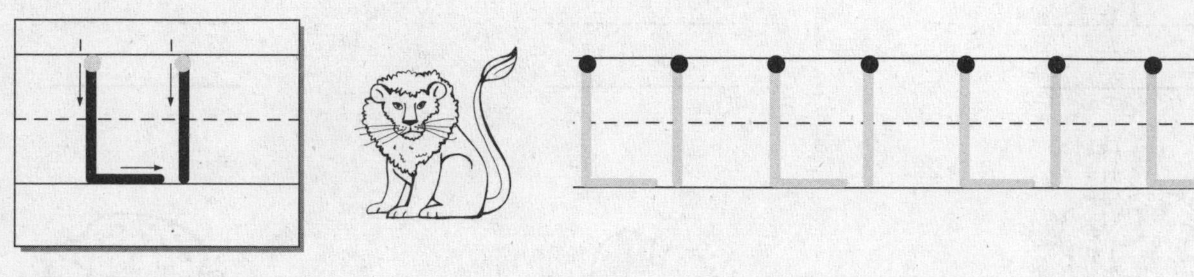

Write a sentence. Use the letters from this page.

TEKS **1.21 (A)** Form upper- and lower-case letters legibly in text, using the basic conventions of print, including spacing between words and sentences.

We can play .

High-Frequency Words:
she, he, said, play

4

We Can

He said, "I can ."

1

TEKS **1.3 (H)** Identify and read at least 100 high-frequency words from a commonly used list.

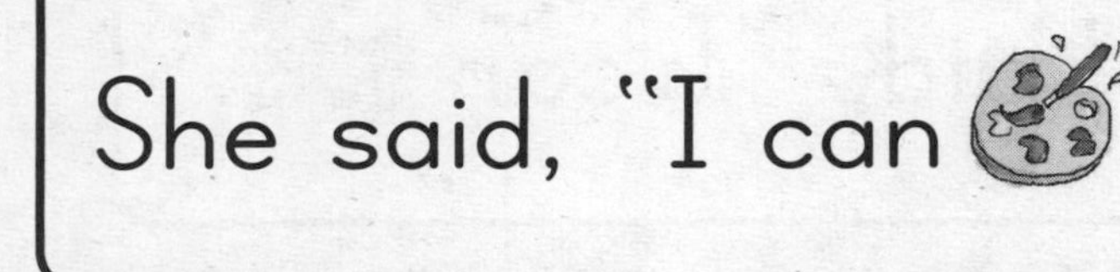

She said, "I can ."

2

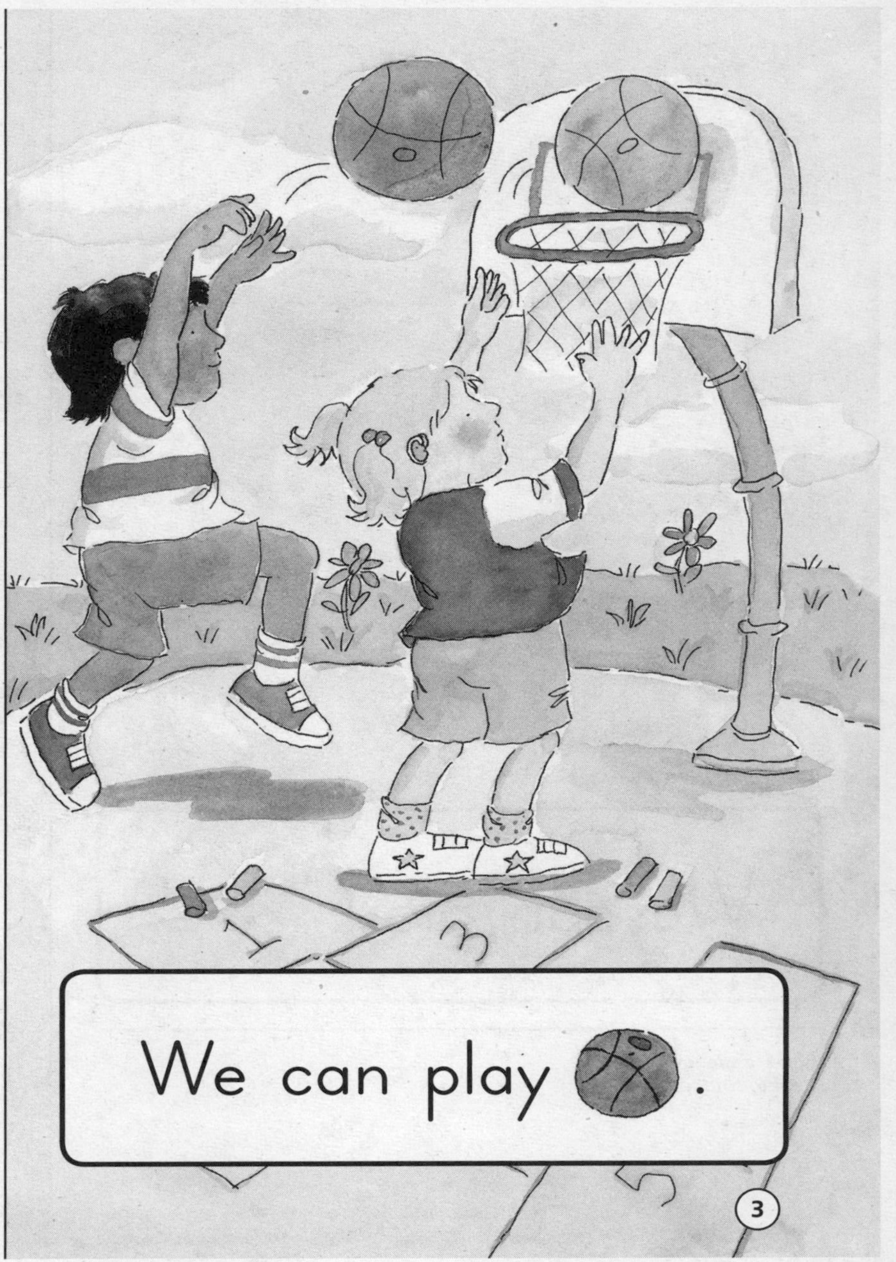

We can play .

3

TEKS **1.3 (H)** Identify and read at least 100 high-frequency words from a commonly used list.

Name ______________________

Say each picture name. Then write a **k** below the picture if its name begins like **king**.

Say each picture name. Then write **ck** below the picture if its name ends like **back**.

Use the letters **ck** to make new words.

ki ______ si ______

Use l letter to make new words.

______ ick ______ ick

TEKS **1.1 (A)** Recognize that spoken words are represented in written English by specific sequences of letters.
1.2 (E) Isolate initial and final sounds in one-syllable spoken words.

Name ________________________________

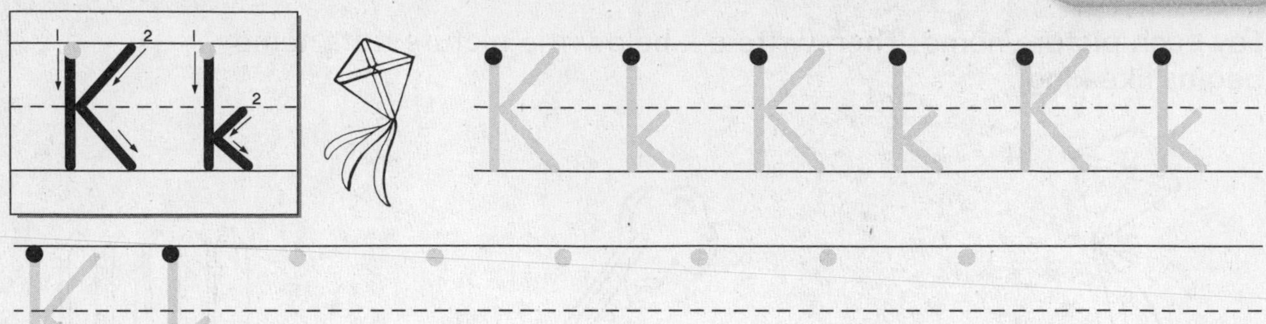

Write some sentences. Use the letters from this page.

TEKS **1.21 (A)** Form upper- and lower-case letters legibly in text, using the basic conventions of print, including spacing between words and sentences.

Name ________________________________

Say each picture name. Then write an **e** below the picture if its name begins like **egg**.

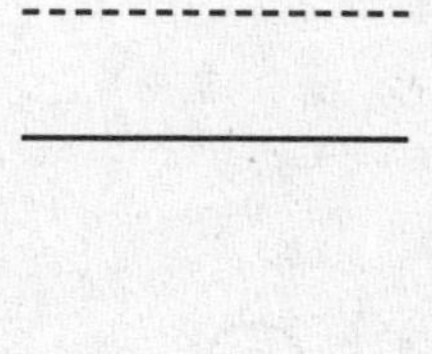

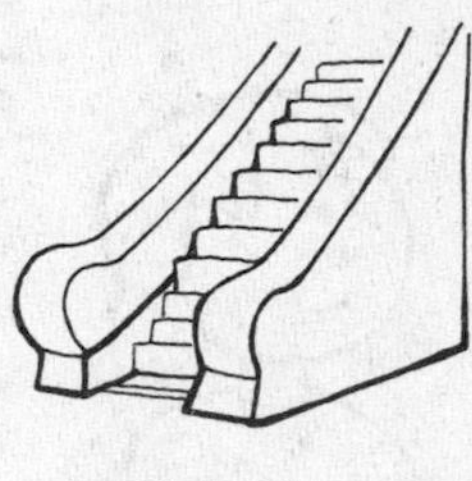

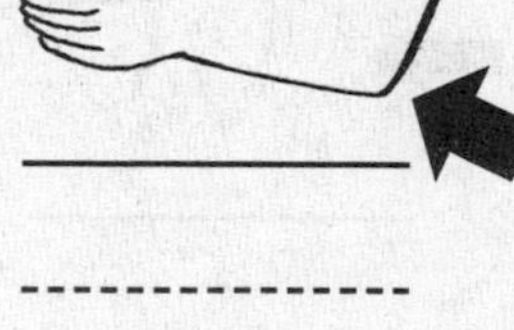

Trace the word **Ed**. Then, practice writing the word **Ed**.

Ed

Write an **e** to complete the word. Then read it.

___gg

TEKS **1.1 (A)** Recognize that spoken words are represented in written English by specific sequences of letters. **1.2 (D)** Blend spoken phonemes to form one-syllable words. **1.2 (E)** Isolate initial sounds in one-syllable spoken words.

Name ______________________

Say each picture name. Then write a **g** below the picture if its name begins like **gate** or a **w** if its name begins like **web**.

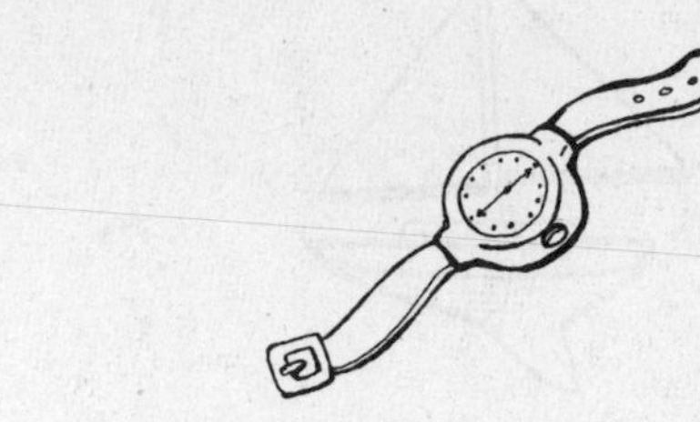

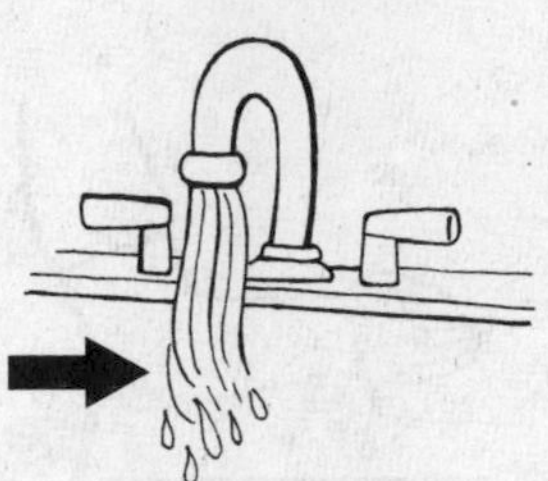

Write **g**, **w**, **s**, or **b** to complete the words. Then read them.

___ et ___ et

___ et ___ et

TEKS **1.1 (A)** Recognize that spoken words are represented in written English by specific sequences of letters. **1.2 (D)** Blend spoken phonemes to form one-syllable words. **1.2 (E)** Isolate initial sounds in one-syllable spoken words.

We like the .

High-Frequency Words:
here, are, what, do, have, is, for

4

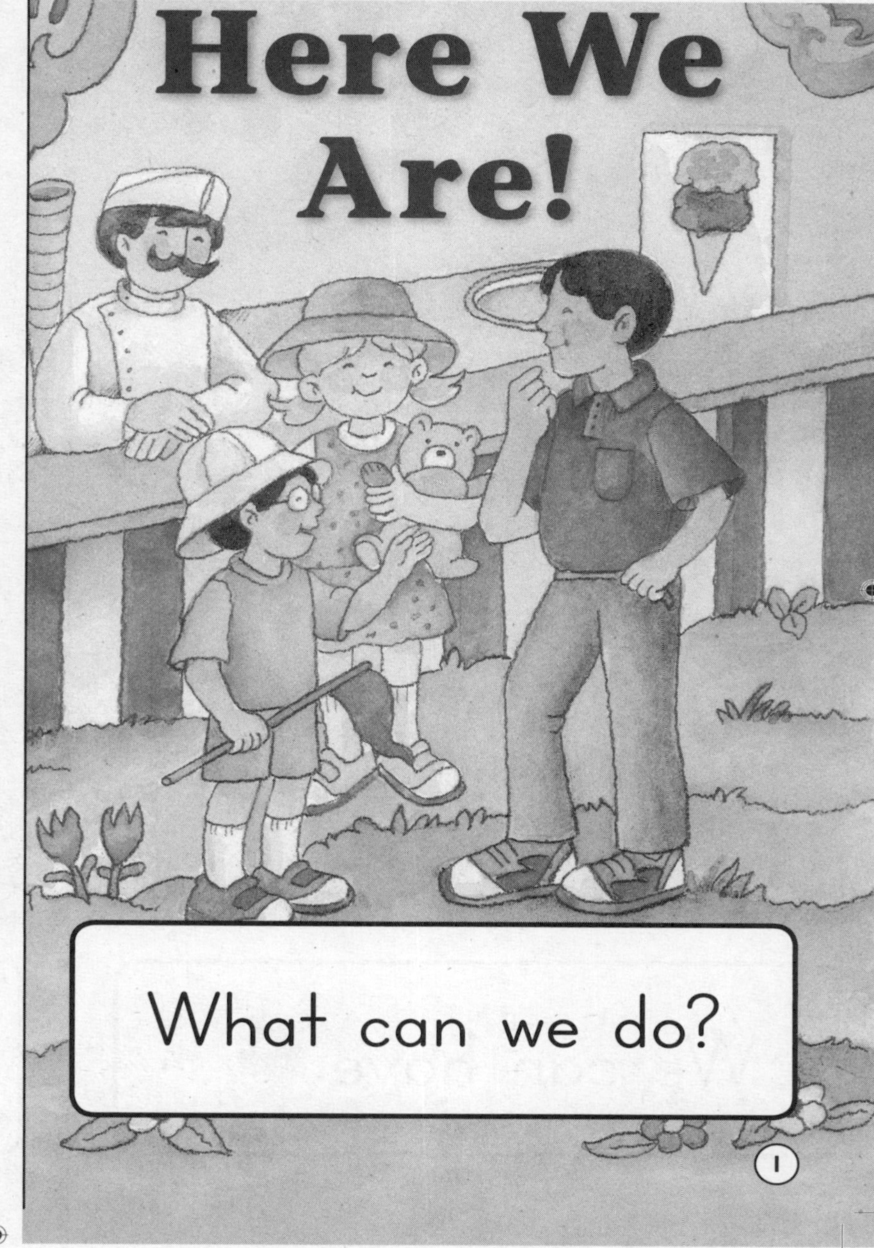

What can we do?

1

TEKS **1.3 (H)** Identify and read at least 100 high-frequency words from a commonly used list.

TEKS **1.3 (H)** Identify and read at least 100 high-frequency words from a commonly used list.

Name ______________________________

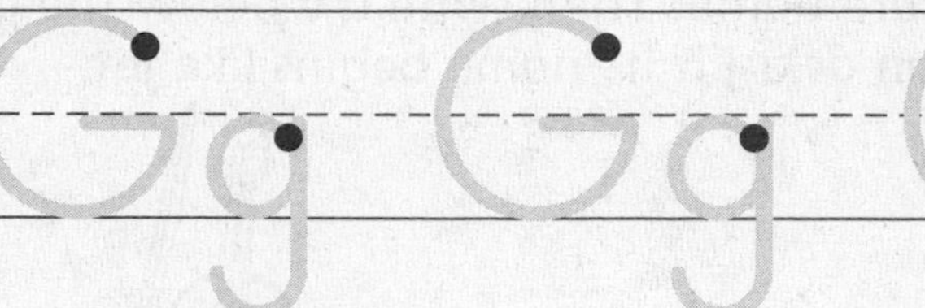

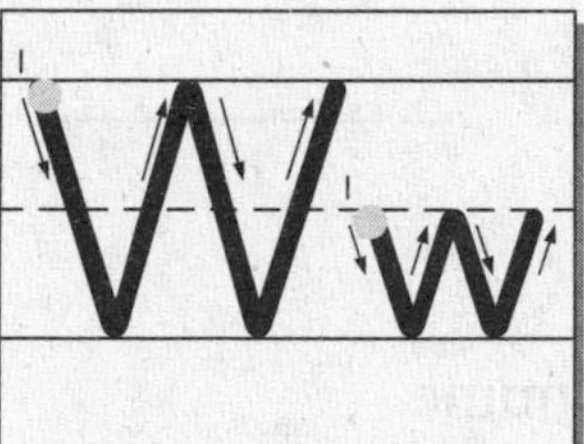
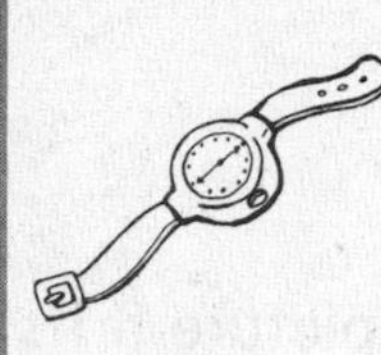
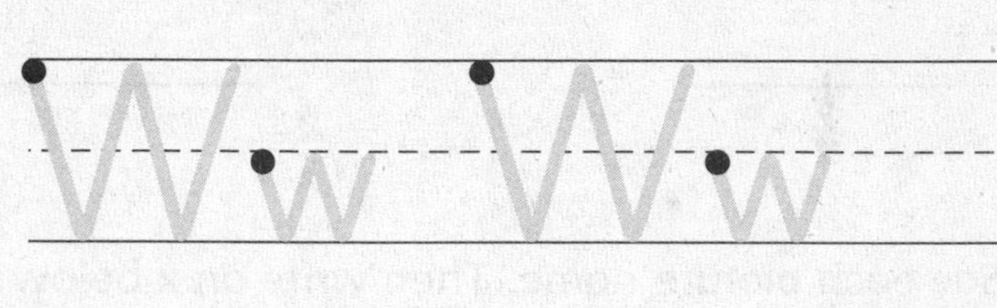

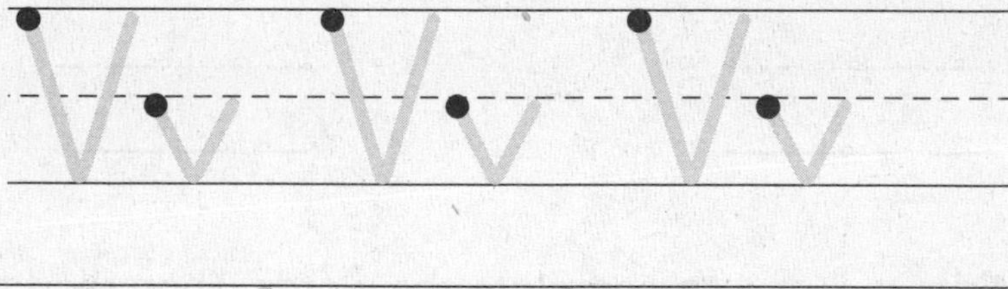

Write a sentence. Use the letters from this page.

TEKS **1.21 (A)** Form upper- and lower-case letters legibly in text, using the basic conventions of print, including spacing between words and sentences.

Name ______________________

Say each picture name. Then write a **v** below the picture if its name begins like **van** or a **j** if its name begins like **jet**.

Say each picture name. Then write an **x** below the picture if its name ends like **fox**.

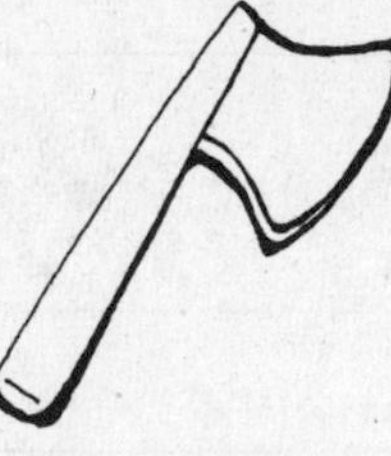

Write **v, j,** or **x** to complete the words. Then read them.

___ an 

___ et 

bo ___ 

TEKS **1.1 (A)** Recognize that spoken words are represented in written English by specific sequences of letters. **1.2 (D)** Blend spoken phonemes to form one-syllable words. **1.2 (E)** Isolate initial and final sounds in one-syllable spoken words.

Name ________________________________

Say each picture name. Then write a **u** below the picture if its name begins like **up**.

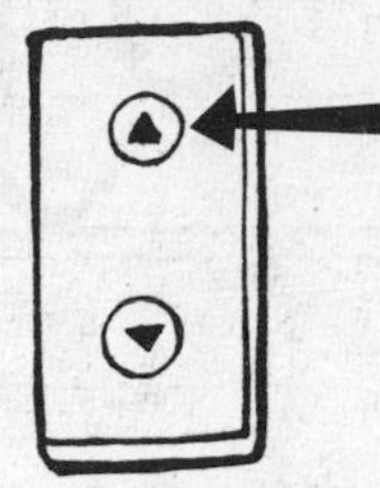

Trace the word **up**. Then practice writing the word **up**.

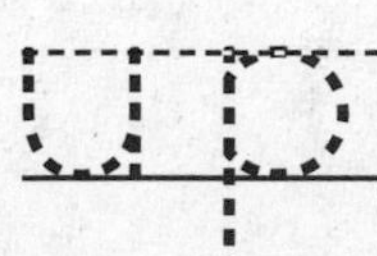

Trace the word **us**. Then practice writing the word **us**.

TEKS **1.1 (A)** Recognize that spoken words are represented in written English by specific sequences of letters. **1.2 (E)** Isolate initial sounds in one-syllable spoken words.

Name ____________________

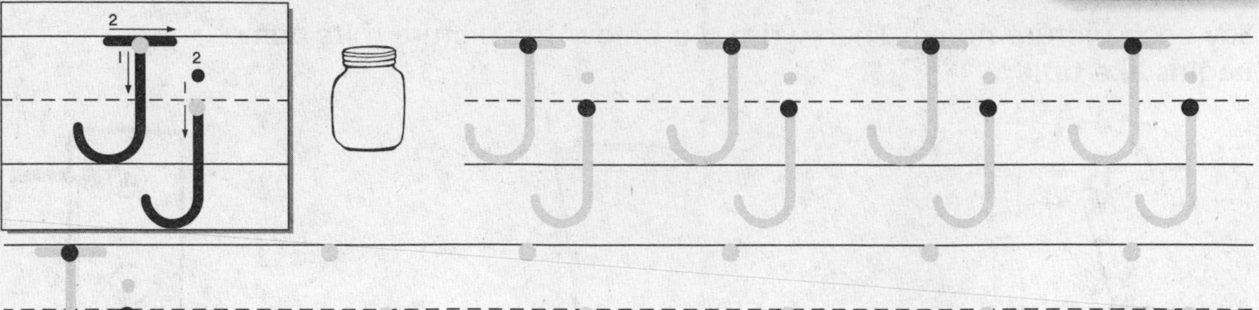

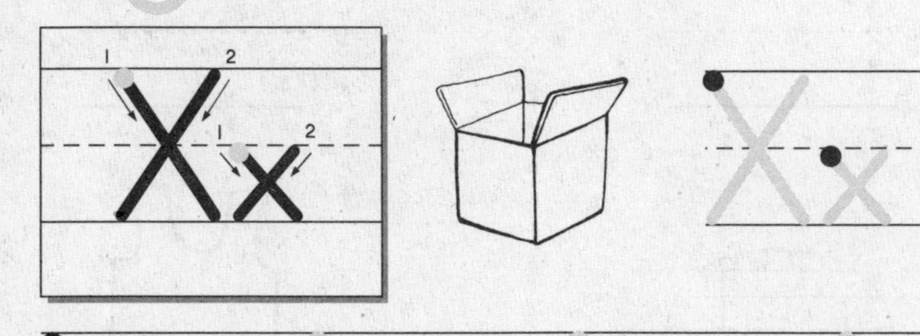

Write a sentence. Use the letters from this page.

TEKS **1.21 (A)** Form upper- and lower-case letters legibly in text, using the basic conventions of print, including spacing between words and sentences.

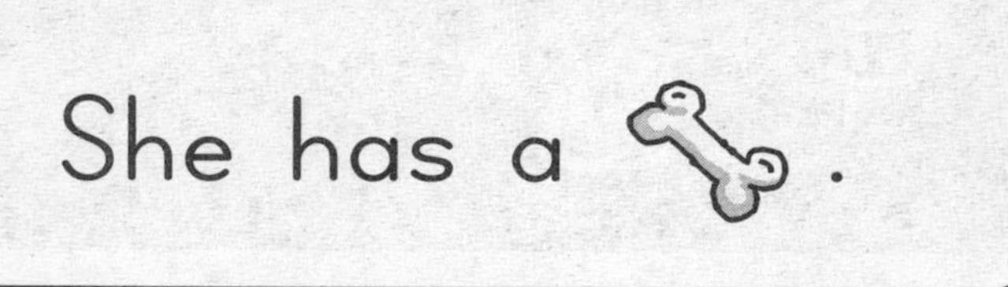

High-Frequency Words:
do, my, look, is, was, has

4

Look and See

Do you see my .

1

TEKS **1.3 (H)** Identify and read at least 100 high-frequency words from a commonly used list.

TEKS **1.3 (H)** Identify and read at least 100 high-frequency words from a commonly used list.

Name ______________________

Say each picture name. Then write a **q** below the picture if its name begins like **queen**, a **y** if it begins like **yarn**, and a **z** if it begins like **zoo**.

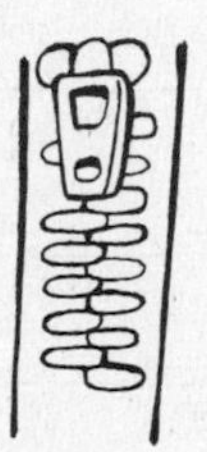

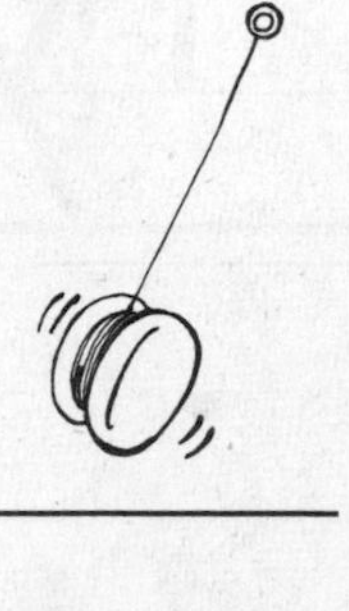

Write **q**, **y**, or **z** to complete the words.

_____ ero 

_____ uilt 

_____ arn 

TEKS **1.1 (A)** Recognize that spoken words are represented in written English by specific sequences of letters. **1.2 (E)** Isolate initial sounds in one-syllable spoken words.

Name ______________________________

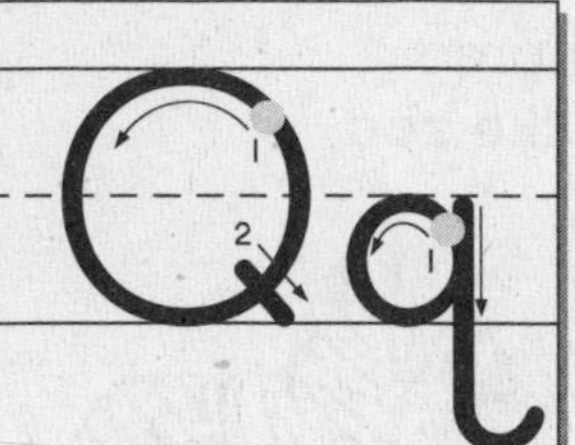

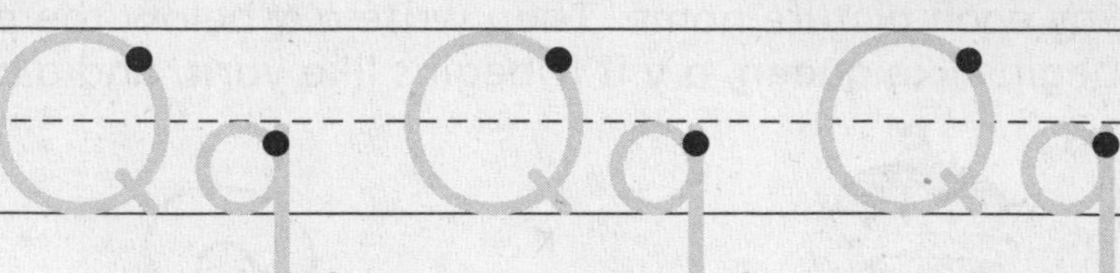

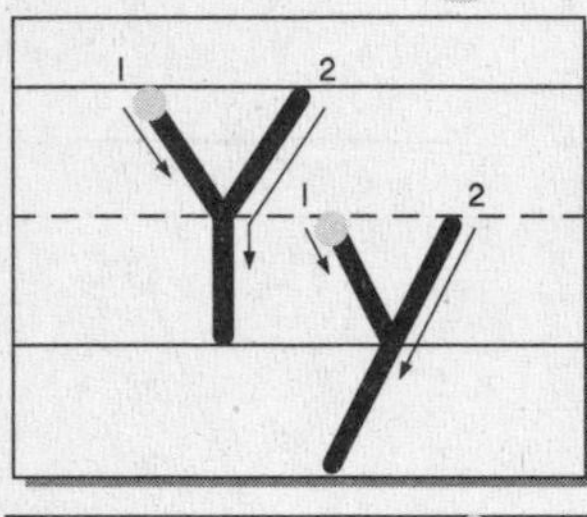

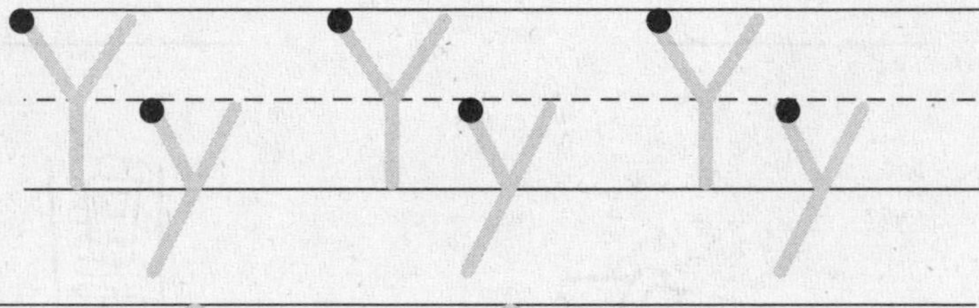

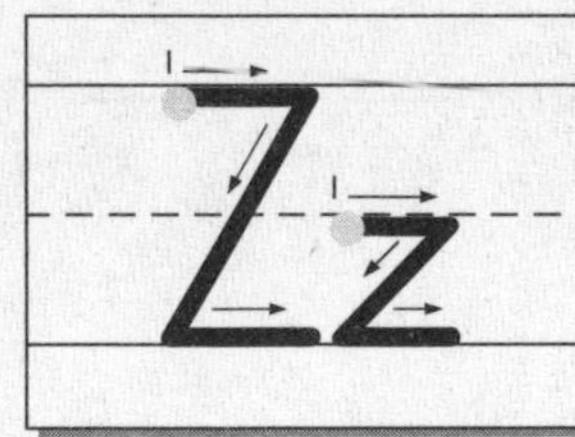

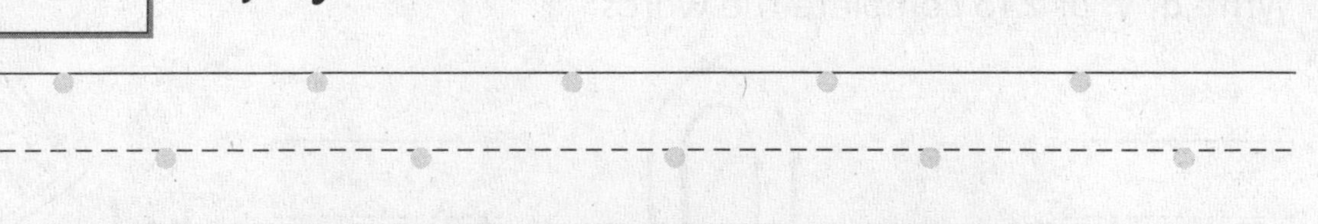

Write a sentence. Use the letters from this page.

TEKS **1.21 (A)** Form upper- and lower-case letters legibly in text, using the basic conventions of print, including spacing between words and sentences.

Name ____________________

Read the word. Circle the picture that it names.

1. cat

2. pan

3. man

4. sat

5. fan

Write a sentence using some of the words. Check that your letters and words are in order left to right.

6. ____________________

TEKS **1.3 (A) (i) (ii)** Decode words in context and in isolation by applying common letter-sound correspondences, including single letters (consonants and vowels).
1.21 (A) Form upper- and lowercase letters legibly in text, using the basic conventions of print.

Name ______________________________

The Princess and the Pea is a fairy tale. A **fairy tale** is a story. It might tell about a king or a queen. It might tell about a prince or a princess. It might tell about magic, too.

Answer each question.

1. What do the words "Once upon a time" tell you? Circle your answer.

   The story happened long ago.

   The story happens today.

2. What happens first? Write your answer.

   ____

   ____

3. The queen helps her son find a wife. How do you help someone? Draw or write your answer.

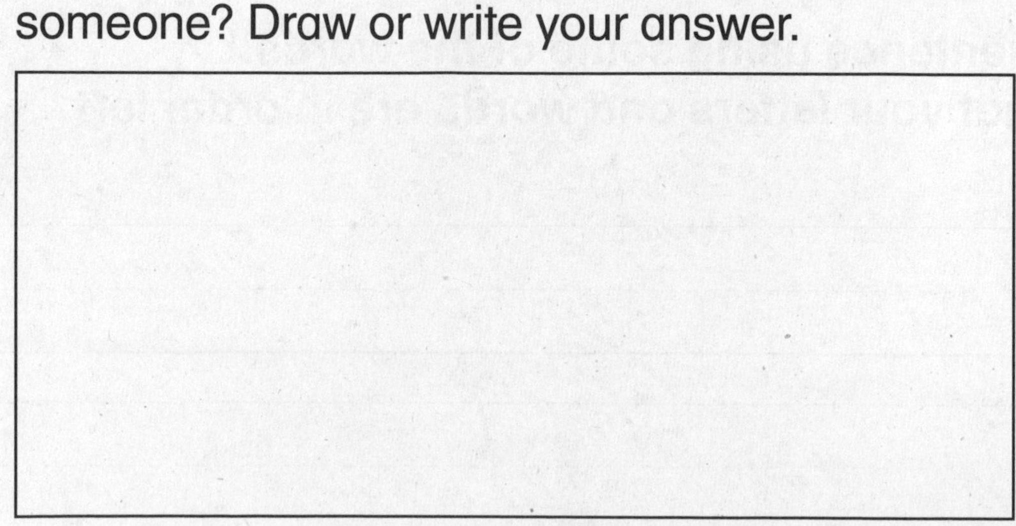

TEKS 1.7 (A) Connect the meaning of a well-known story to personal experiences.
1.7 (B) Explain the function of recurring phrases in traditional fairy tales.
1.9 (A) Retell a story's beginning, middle, and end with attention to the sequence of events.

Name ______________________________

Complete each sentence.
Use one of the words in the box.

up	not	jump

1. I can ________________.

2. The cat ran ________________.

3. The cat is ________________ little.

Write your own sentence using a word from the box.
Check that you have left a space between words.

4. ____

____

TEKS **1.3 (H)** Identify and read at least 100 high-frequency words from a commonly used list. **1.21 (A)** Form upper- and lowercase letters legibly in text, using the basic conventions of print, including spacing between words and sentences.

Name ____________________

Practice

Structural Analysis: Inflectional Ending *-s*

Circle the word that names each picture.

Then write the word.

1. 
cat cats

2. 
man map

3. 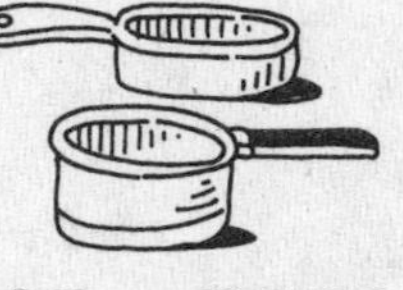
pan pans

4. 
rats rat

5. 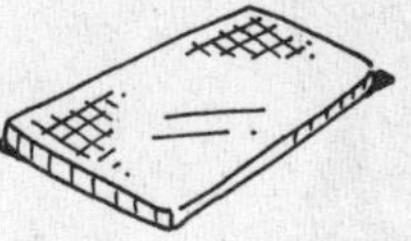
mat mats

6. 
can cans

7. 
fans fan

8. 
hat hats

TEKS **1.20 (A) (ii)** Understand and use singular and plural nouns in the context of reading, writing, and speaking.
1.22 (D) Spell base words with inflectional endings.

Name ______________________________

As you read Pam and Sam, fill in the Character Chart. Use words from the story.

Pam Can	Sam Can

How does the Character Chart help you tell about the characters in Pam and Sam?

TEKS 1.9 (B) Describe characters in a story.

Name ______________________

Look at the pictures. Read the story.

Nat is a cat.
Nat can go up.
Nat can go down.
Pam and Sam look for Nat.
Pam is sad.
Where is Nat?

Write T if the sentence is true.
Write F if the sentence is false.

1. Nat is a cat. ____

2. Nat can go up and down. ____

3. Pam is not sad. ____

Write a sentence to answer the question.
Write capital and lowercase letters clearly left to right.

4. Why is Pam sad? ______________________

____

Name ______________________________

Look at the pictures. Write 1, 2, and 3 to show the order in which things happen.

A.

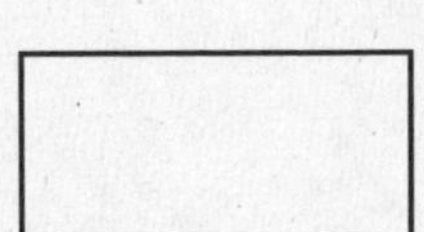

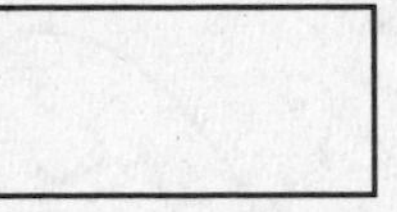

B. Think about the pictures you labeled. Write a word that tells what is happening in the second picture.

____

C. Tell about something that you read this week.

____

Title ______________________________

Author ______________________________

What I Read About ______________________________

TEKS **1.9 (A)** Retell a story's beginning, middle, and end with attention to the sequence of events. **1.19 (C)** Write brief comments on literary or informational texts.

Name ______________________________

Photographs are pictures that show people, animals, and things in real life.

Look at the picture.
Read the sentence that tells about the picture.

Look! My little cat is here.

Write your own sentence about the picture.
Check that your capital and lowercase letters are clear.

____

____

TEKS 1.21 (A) Form upper- and lower-case letters legibly in text, using the basic conventions of print.

Name ______________________________

As I read, I will pay attention to the intonation.

Sam has a mat.
04 Can Pam?
06 Sam has a cap.
10 Can Pam?
12 Pam ran with the cap.
17 Pam can tap!
20 Tap, Pam, tap! 23

Comprehension Check

1. What does Sam have?

2. What can Pam do?

	Words Read	–	Number of Errors	=	Words Correct Score
First Read		–		=	
Second Read		–		=	

TEKS 1.3 (I) Monitor accuracy of decoding.
1.5 Read aloud grade-level appropriate text with fluency and comprehension.

Name ______________________________

Look at this story. Draw a box around the first word that you should read. Then point to each word as you read the story aloud.

Pat has a cat.
The cat can jump.
The cat can run.

Read the story aloud again.
Circle the capital letters.
Underline the lowercase letters.

Use the letters in the box to complete part of the alphabet. Make sure that the letters are in the right order.

a	G	c	h	F	e

A ____ B b C ____ D d E ____

____ f ____ g H ____ I i J j

TEKS 1.1 (A) Recognize that spoken words are represented in written English with specific sequences of letters. 1.1 (B) Identify upper- and lowercase letters. 1.1 (C) Sequence the letters of the alphabet.

Name ______________________________

Use the words from the box to name each picture.

cat	hat	bat	pan	can	fan

1. ______________________________

2. ______________________________

3. ______________________________

4. ______________________________

5. ______________________________

6. ______________________________

TEKS **1.3 (A) (i) (ii)** Decode words in isolation by applying common letter-sound correspondences, including single letters (consonants and vowels).

Name ___________________________

The Great Rope Tug is an African folktale. A **folktale** is an old story. Adults tell folktales to children. Some folktales teach something.

Answer each question.

1. What makes Rabbit mad? Write your answer.

____

2. What words from the story name animals? Circle the animals in this list.

rabbit	elephant	jump
Pam	over	hippo

3. How does the rope tug end? Draw or write your answer.

TEKS 1.6 (D) Identify and sort words into conceptual categories. 1.9 (A) Retell a story's beginning, middle, and end with attention to the sequence of events. 1.9 (B) Describe characters in a story and the reasons for their feelings.

Name ____________________

Fill in the sentences using the words in the box.

too	It	over

1. ______________ is in the box.

2. You have fun, ______________!

3. It is ______________ Pam.

TEKS 1.3 (H) Identify and read at least 100 high-frequency words from a commonly used list.

Name ____________________

Practice

Structural Analysis: Inflectional Ending -s

Circle the word that completes each sentence. Then write the word on the line.

1. Sam ____________.

nap naps

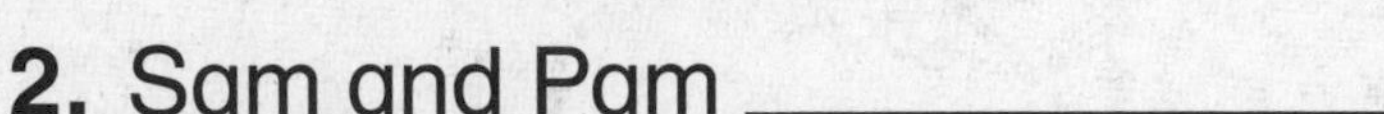

2. Sam and Pam ____________.

play plays

3. Pam ____________.

pack packs

4. Pam ____________ go with Sam.

can cans

5. Pam ____________ at Sam.

look looks

TEKS **1.20 (A) (i)** Understand and use present-tense verbs in the context of reading, writing, and speaking.

Name ______________________________

As you read I Can Too!, fill in the Sequence Chart. Use words from the story.

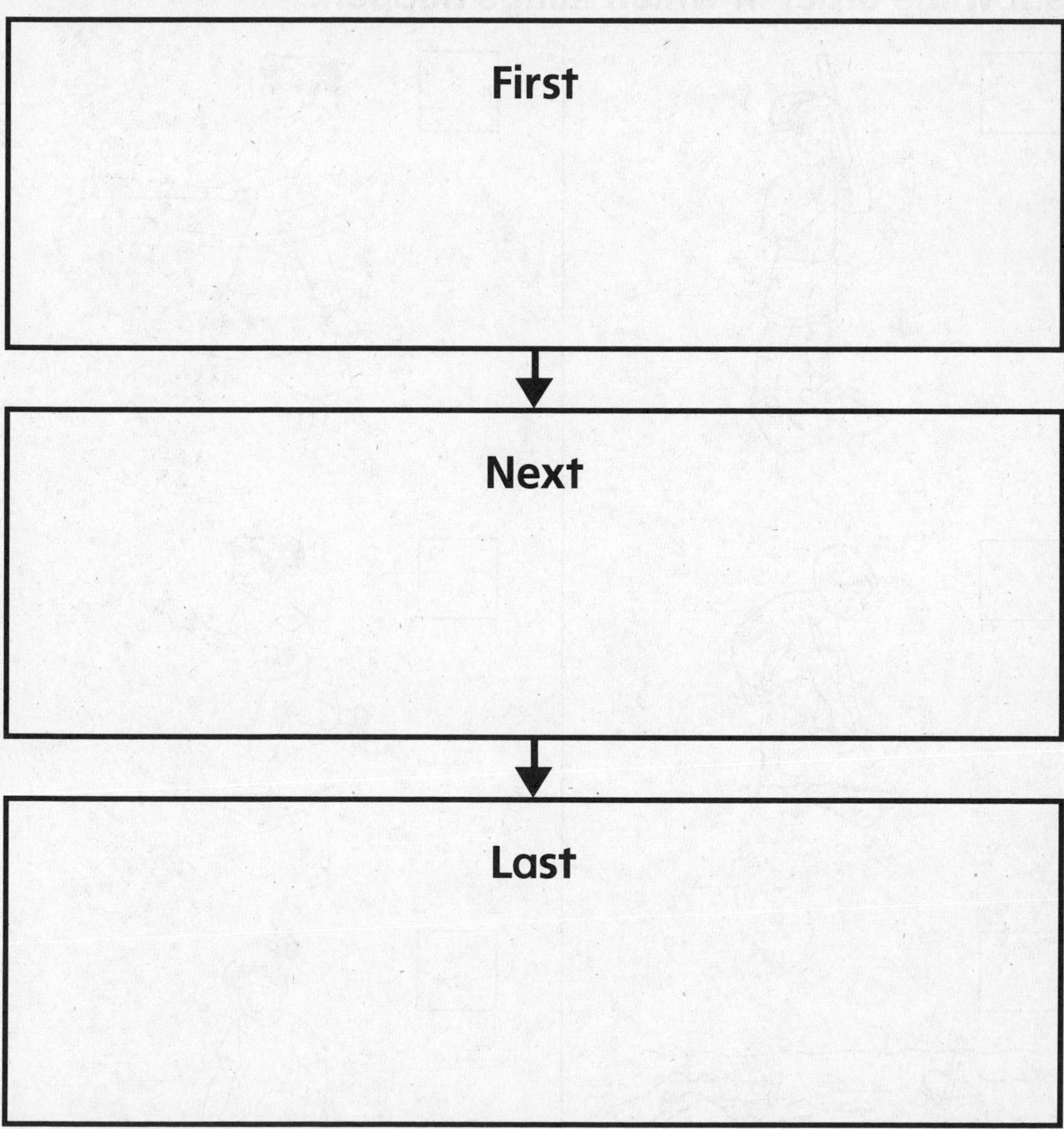

How does the Sequence Chart help you retell the events at the beginning, middle, and end of I Can Too!?

TEKS **1.9 (A)** Retell a story's beginning, middle, and end with attention to the sequence of events.

Name ________________________________

Look at the pictures.
Write 1, 2, and 3 for each column of pictures to show the order in which things happen.

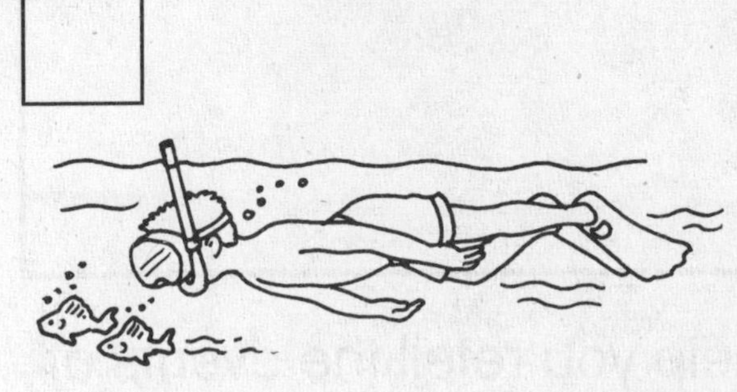

TEKS **1.9 (A)** Retell a story's beginning, middle, and end with attention to the sequence of events.

Name ______________________

Words that **rhyme** end with the same sound. **Rhythm** is when words and sounds repeat to give a poem a beat.

A. Circle the pictures that rhyme.

1.

2.

B. Read the poem.

Pat the cat
sat on a hat.

Pat the cat
sat on the mat.

3. Underline the words that repeat.

4. Write two words that rhyme.

____

TEKS 1.8 Respond to and use rhythm and rhyme in poetry.

Name ______________________________

Labels give information about a picture.

Look at the picture. Read the labels.

Write the word that completes each sentence.

1. The man has a ______________.

2. Pam has a ______________.

3. The cat has a ______________.

4. Sam has a ______________.

TEKS 1.14 (D) Use text features to locate specific information in text.

Name ______________________________________

As I read, I will pay attention to pauses for sentence punctuation.

Mack can jump up.
04 Mack can tag a pal.
09 Mack can bat.
12 Can Mack nap?
15 Mack can not! 18

Comprehension Check

1. What can Mack do?

2. Who could not nap?

	Words Read	–	Number of Errors	=	Words Correct Score
First Read		–		=	
Second Read		–		=	

TEKS **1.3 (I)** Monitor accuracy of decoding.
1.5 Read aloud grade-level appropriate text with fluency and comprehension.

Name ______________________

Practice

Concepts of Print

A. Identify the uppercase and lowercase letters. Point to each letter as you read it. Then draw a line to match each uppercase and lowercase letter.

d	e	r	g	o	k	l	b	w	i
L	D	B	R	W	I	G	E	O	K

B. Write the correct letter of the alphabet on the line. Write a lowercase letter.

1. c ______ e

2. m ______ o

3. p ______ r

4. j ______ l

TEKS 1.1 (B) Identify upper- and lower-case letters.
1.1 (C) Sequence the letters of the alphabet.

Name ____________________

The letter **i** stands for the middle sound in **big** and **fin.**

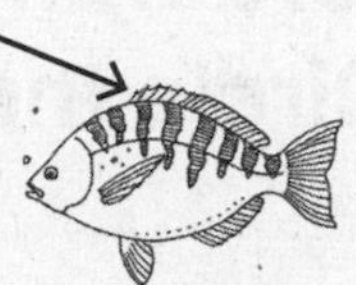

Read the words in the box. Then write the word that names each picture.

pig	kick	pin	sit

1. ____________________

3. ____________________

2. ____________________

4. ____________________

Write your own sentence using words from the box. Check that your capital and lowercase letters are clear.

5. ____________________

TEKS **1.3 (A) (i) (ii)** Decode words in context and in isolation by applying common letter-sound correspondences, including single letters (consonants and vowels).
1.21 (A) Form upper- and lower-case letters legibly in text, using the basic conventions of print.

Name ____________________

Write the word from the box that completes each sentence. Circle the picture that goes with the sentence.

be	ride	run

1. Nan will ____________ here.

2. My cat can ____________ here with me.

3. I can ____________ with Nat.

Write your own sentence. Use a word from the box. Leave a space between the words in your sentence.

____

TEKS 1.3 (H) Identify and read at least 100 high-frequency words from a commonly used list. 1.21 (A) Form upper- and lowercase letters legibly in text, using the basic conventions of print.

Name ______________________________

Practice

Structural Analysis: Double Final Consonants

Some words end in the same two consonants.

will **jazz** **pass**

Read each sentence.
Underline the word that ends with the same two consonants. Write the word on the line.

1. Matt runs to his little cat.

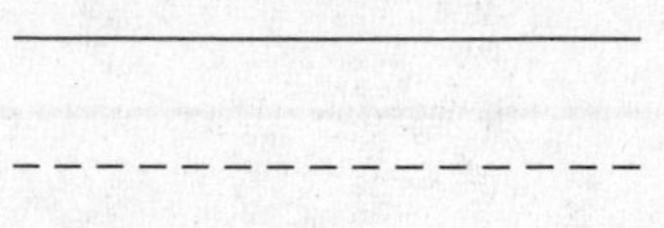

2. Pam rides to the hill.

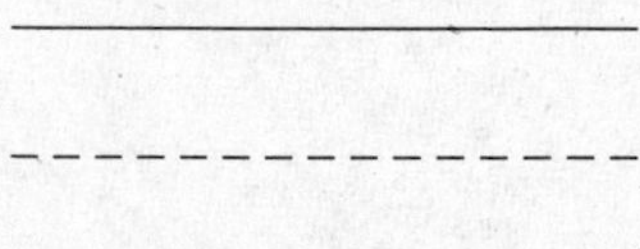

3. I kiss my Dad.

4. The mitt is on the ride.

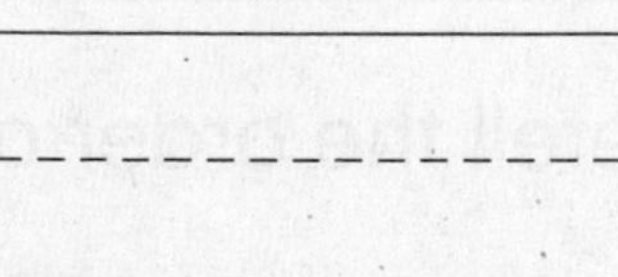

TEKS **1.3 (A) (i) (ii)** Decode words in context by applying common letter-sound correspondences, including single letters (consonants and vowels).

Name ______________________________

As you read How You Grew, fill in the Sequence Chart. Use words from the story.

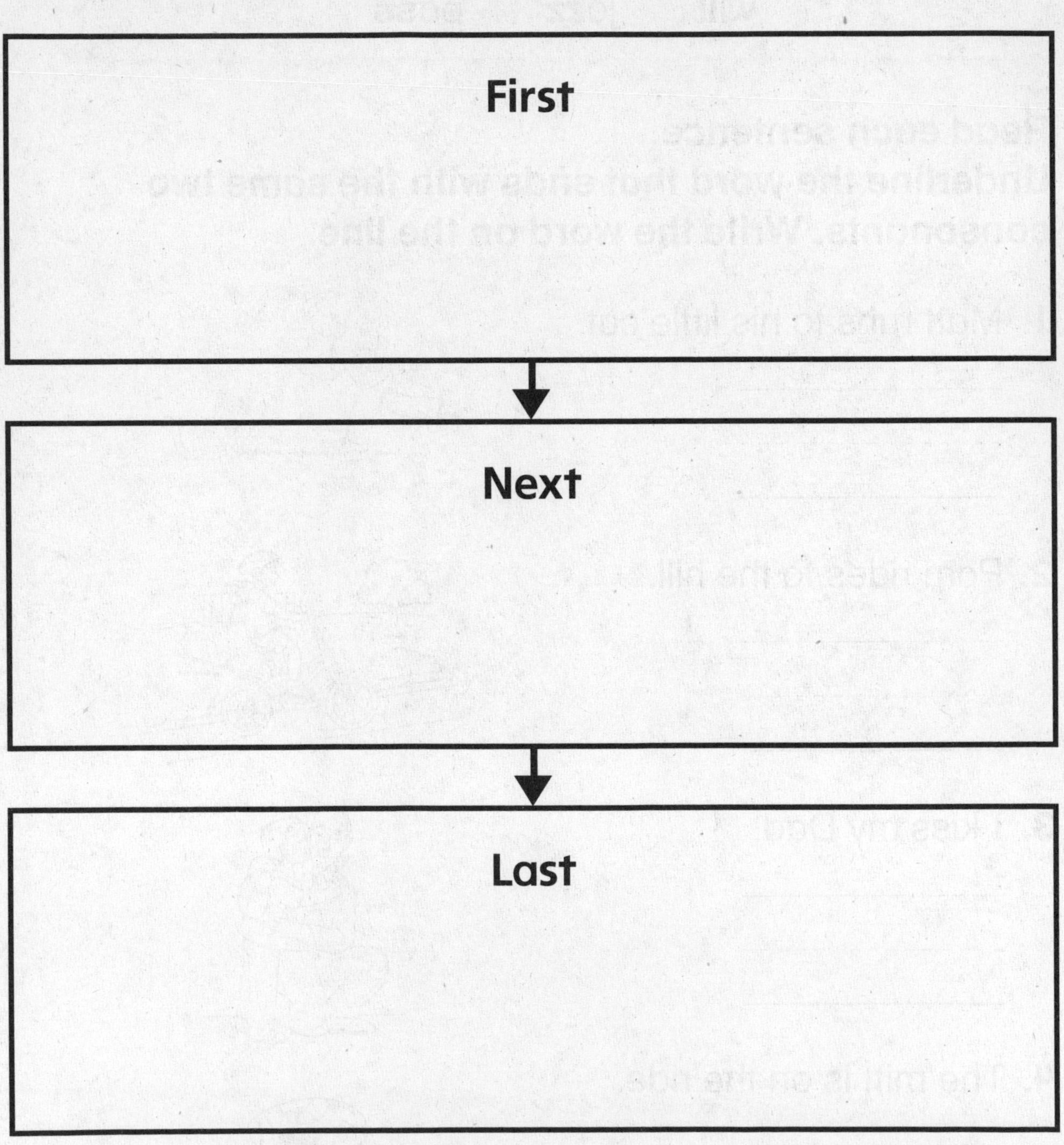

How does the Sequence Chart help you retell the order of events in How You Grew?

____

TEKS 1.14 (C) Retell the order of events in a text by referring to the words.

Name ______________________________

Look at the pictures.
Read the sentences.

1. 
2. 
3. 
4. 

The ball is down.
My cat and I play ball.
My cat runs down, too.
My cat plays with a ball.

Write the sentences in the correct order on the lines.

1. ______________________________

2. ______________________________

3. ______________________________

4. ______________________________

TEKS 1.14 (C) Retell the order of events in a text by referring to the words and illustrations.

Name ______________________________

Look at the pictures. Read the sentences.

The cat plays. 1.

Now the cat is big. 2.

The cat is little. 3.

Write the sentences in the correct order on the lines. Read them to retell the events.

1. ______________________________

2. ______________________________

3. ______________________________

TEKS 1.14 (C) Retell the order of events in a text by referring to the words and illustrations.

Name ______________________________

Nonfiction gives us information about real people, places, and things. When nonfiction authors tell about things that really happened, they put the events in order.

1. Look at the pictures. Write 1, 2, or 3 to show the order in which things happen.

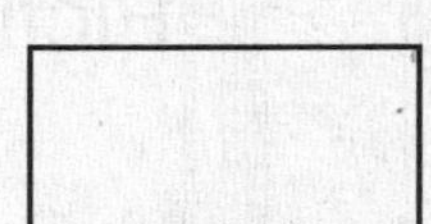

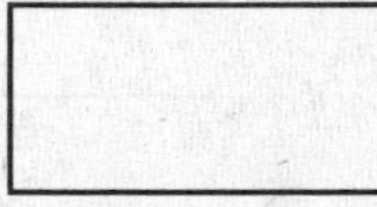

2. How does the girl feel at the end of the story? Draw a face in the circle.

3. What is the girl doing?

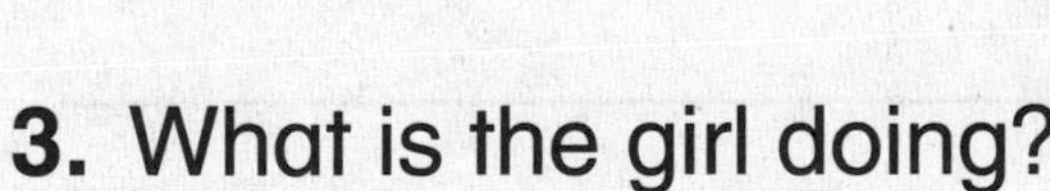

TEKS **1.14 (A)** Restate the main idea, heard or read. **1.14 (B)** Identify important details in text, heard or read. **1.14 (C)** Retell the order of events in a text by referring to the illustrations.

The **title** of a book is the name of the book.
The **author** of a book writes the story.
The **illustrator** makes the pictures.

Look at the book cover. Answer the questions.

1. Who wrote the book?

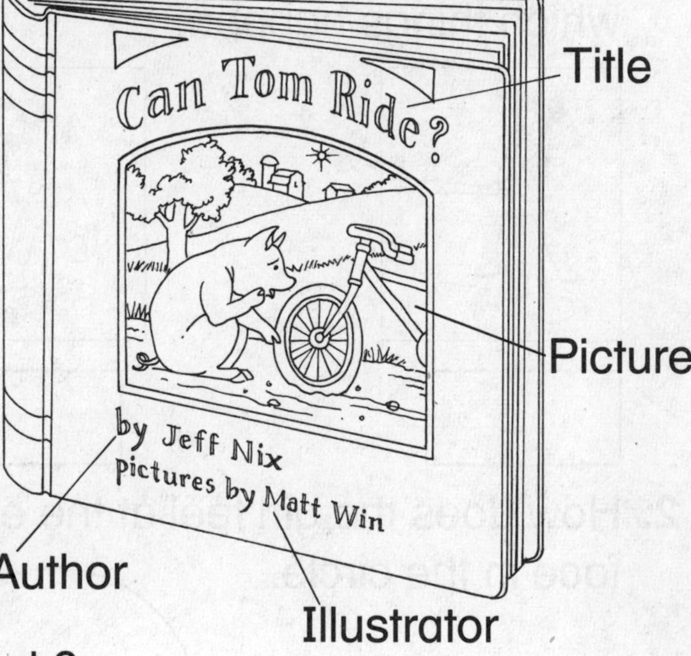

2. Who made the picture?

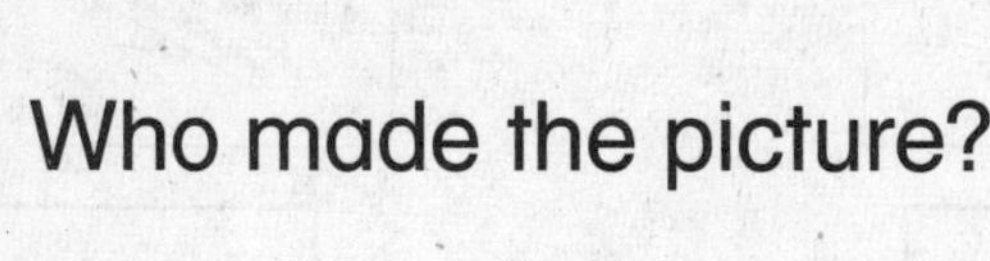

3. What is the title of the book?

4. What picture is on the cover?

TEKS 1.1 (F) Identify the information that different parts of a book provide.
1.14 (D) Use text features to locate specific information in text.

Name ______________________

Practice

Fluency: Choral Read: Intonation

As I read, I will pay attention to the exclamation marks.

"Can I hit, too?"
04 said Jim to Zack.
08 Jim is at bat.
12 Jim sits back as he hits!
18 Jim had a big, big rip.
24 Dad can fix it!
28 Jim has his bat back.
33 Jim did not quit!
37 "I hit it over!" said Jim.
43 "Yip! Yip! Yip!" said Tip. 48

Comprehension Check

1. What does Dad do?
2. What does Jim do?

	Words Read	–	Number of Errors	=	Words Correct Score
First Read		–		=	
Second Read		–		=	

TEKS **1.3 (I)** Monitor accuracy of decoding.
1.5 Read aloud grade-level appropriate text with fluency and comprehension.

Name ______________________________

Practice

Concepts of Print

Every sentence begins with a capital letter.

Every sentence ends with a special mark.

Read this story aloud. Answer the questions.

I can sit.
I can run.
I am six.
Now I am big!

1. Draw a box around the first word you should read.
2. Find these words in the story. Draw a box around them.

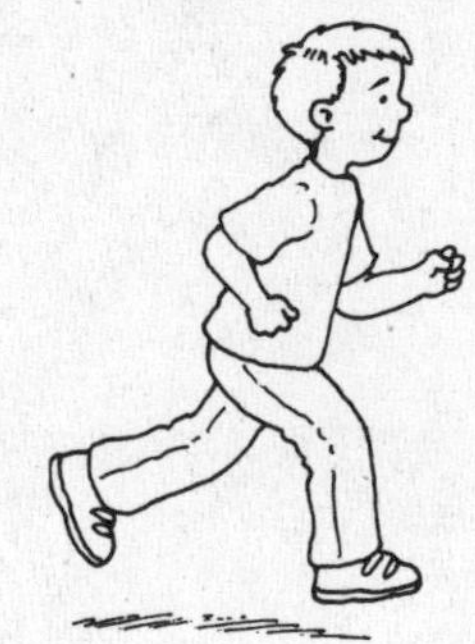

3. Draw a circle around a capital letter at the beginning of a sentence.
4. What letter follows the letter I in the alphabet? ______
5. Draw a line under an end mark at the end of a sentence.

TEKS **1.1 (A)** Recognize that spoken words are represented in written English with specific sequences of letters. **1.1 (B)** Identify upper-case letters. **1.1 (C)** Sequence the letters of the alphabet. **1.1 (D)** Recognize the distinguishing features of a sentence.

Name ______________________

Practice

Phonics: l Blends

Blend the first two letters to read each word.

black **cl**ap **fl**ag **cl**ip **sl**ip

Use the words in the box to name each picture.

1.  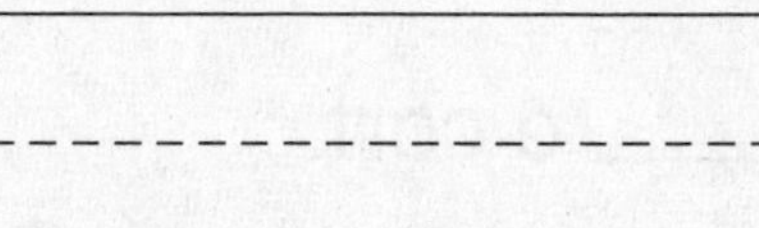 ______________________

2. ______________________

3. 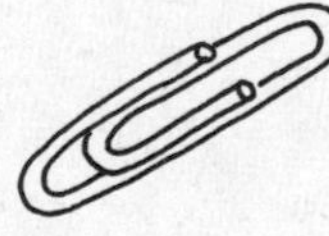 ______________________

4.  

____

5.  ______________________

TEKS 1.3 (A) (iii) Decode words in isolation by applying common letter-sound correspondences, including consonant blends.

Name ______________________________

Write the word from the box that completes each sentence. Circle the picture that goes with each sentence.

come	good	pull	down

1. It can ______________ a cart.

2. It can swim ______________ in the pond.

3. She will ______________ if you call her.

4. He is ______________ at sleeping.

TEKS **1.3 (H)** Identify and read at least 100 high-frequency words from a commonly used list.

Name ______________________

Practice

Structural Analysis: Possessives with *'s*

When **'s** is added to a word, it means that something belongs to that person or thing.

Circle the correct word and write it on the line.

1. This is ______________ pet.

   Fran   Fran's

2. This is ______________ bag.

   Gram's   Gram

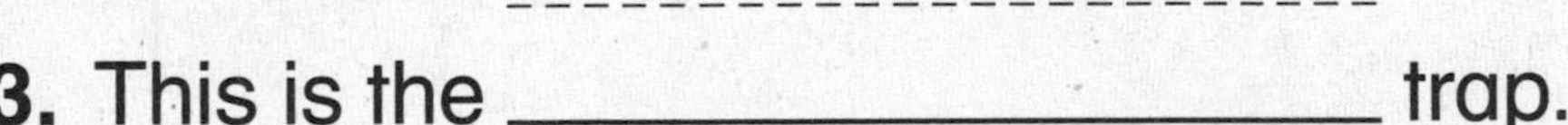

3. This is the ______________ trap.

   crab   crab's

4. This is ______________ crib.

   Jim's   Jim

Write your own sentence. Use 's to show something belongs. Write your capital and lowercase letters clearly.

____

TEKS **1.21 (A)** Form upper- and lower-case letters legibly in text, using the basic conventions of print.

Name ________________________________

As you read Flip, fill in the Plot Chart.

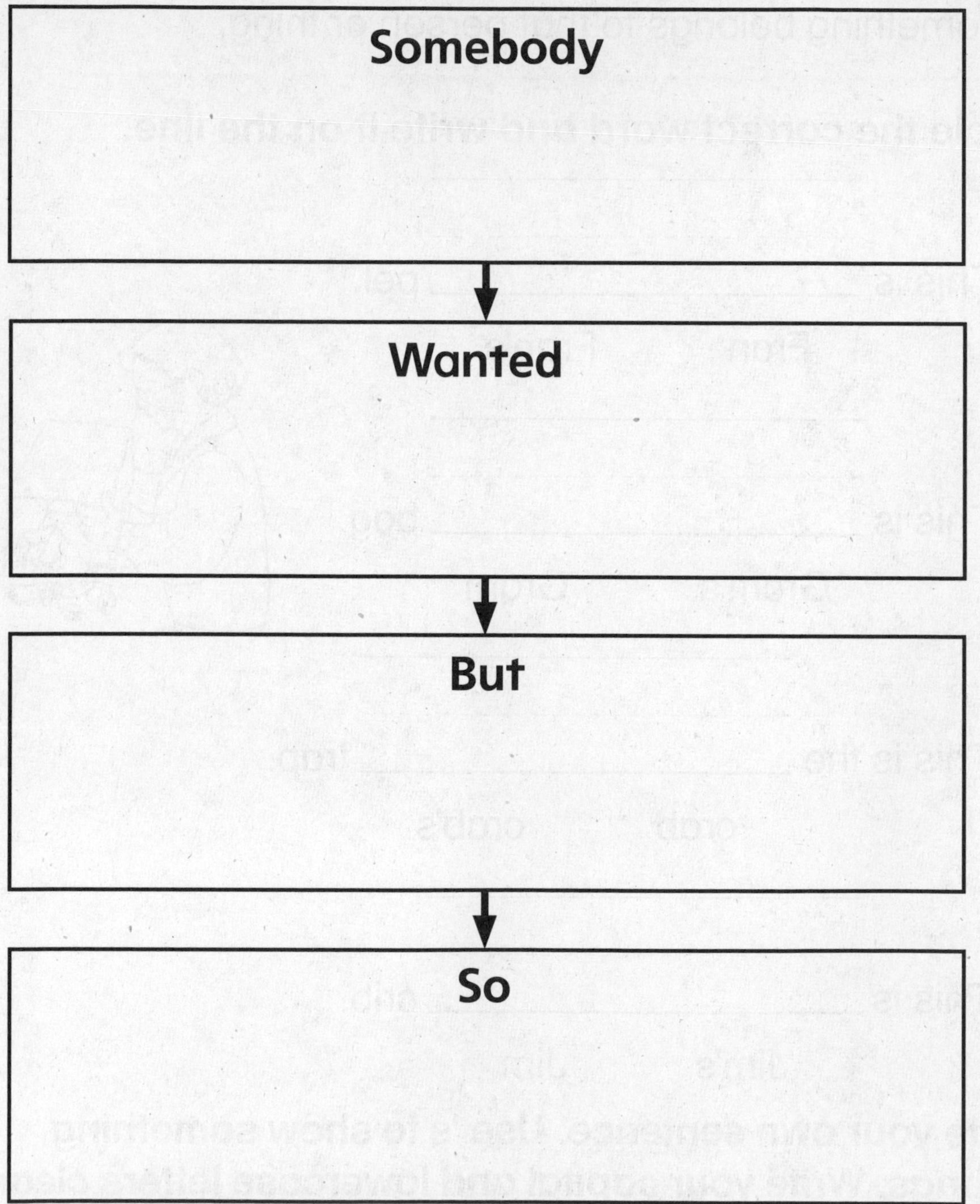

How does the Plot Chart help you better understand the problem and solution in Flip?

TEKS 1.9 (A) Describe the plot (problem and solution).

Name ______________________________

Read the story.

The Baby Bunny

All the baby bunnies were sleeping in their nest. One baby woke up. He planned to have some fun. The bunny left the nest.

What a big place he saw! The bunny hopped and jumped. He had a good time. Then the rain fell. The baby bunny wished he was safe in his cozy nest.

Just then, he saw his mom. She was calling his name. The baby bunny hopped to his mom. They went back home. He was glad.

Read the sentences. Write P for the problem. Write S for the solution.

1. The rain came. ______
2. The bunny saw his mom. ______
3. The bunny wished he was in the nest. ______
4. The bunny went home. ______

TEKS 1.9 (A) Describe the plot (problem and solution).

Name ________________________

Practice

Comprehension: Analyze Story Structure

A. Read the story.

Pip the big pig had a good day. His friend Pat the cat did, too. First, Pip sat in the sun. Pat sat in the sun, too. Pip took a nap. Pat did, too. Then Pip did six flips. Pat did six flips, too. Last, Pat took a ride on Pip's back.

B. Read the sentences. Write B for the beginning sentences, M for the middle sentences, and E for the end sentences.

1. Pip took a nap. ____________

2. Pip sat in the sun. ____________

3. Pat did six flips. ____________

TEKS **1.9 (A)** Retell a story's beginning, middle, and end with attention to the sequence of events.

Name ______________________________

Nonfiction tells about real people, places, and things. Nonfiction may contain facts, dates, and names.

Read the sentences. Answer the questions.

Cats can jump.

Cats can nap.

Cats can run.

1. Write a word that tells what the sentences are about.

____

2. Write three words that tell facts about cats.

____

TEKS 1.14 (A) Restate the main idea, heard or read.
1.14 (B) Identify important facts in text, heard or read.

Practice

Text Feature: Lists

Name ______________________________

A **list** is a series of things written in order.

1. nap 

2. sit up and beg 

3. wag 

4. play 

Write two things from the list that pets can do.

____

____

TEKS 1.14 (D) Use text features to locate specific information in text.

Name ______________________________

Practice

Fluency: Choral Read: Intonation

As I read, I will pay attention to the exclamation marks.

Sam is a clam.
04 Sam has a black back.
09 Sam can not run.
13 Sam can not ride.
17 Flip, flap, flip!
20 Sam can be big.
24 Flip, flap, slam!
27 Sam can be flat.
31 Clap, clap, clap!
34 Sam the Clam is glad. 39

Comprehension Check

1. What can Sam the Clam not do?

2. What does Sam do to be big and then flat?

	Words Read	–	Number of Errors	=	Words Correct Score
First Read		–		=	
Second Read		–		=	

TEKS **1.3 (I)** Monitor accuracy of decoding.
1.5 Read aloud grade-level appropriate text with fluency and comprehension.

Name ______________________________

A. Look at the story. Draw a box around the first word you should read. Read the story aloud.

I had a cat. It sat on Dad's cap.
I had a duck. It sat on Mom's mat.
I had a pig. It kicked Kit.
I got a bird. It is just right.

1. Find a capital letter in the story. Circle it.
2. Find these words in the story. Draw a line under them.

3. Add an end mark to this sentence.

Sam is my cat ______

B. On the line, write the next letter in the alphabet. Write a lowercase letter.

4. f, g, ______

5. m, n, ______

TEKS 1.1 (B) Identify upper- and lower-case letters. 1.1 (C) Sequence the letters of the alphabet. 1.1 (D) Recognize the distinguishing features of a sentence.

Name ______________________________

Sometimes consonants form a **blend**. You can hear each consonant sound in a **final blend**.

ha**nd** pa**st**

Say the word. Draw a line under the final blend. Write the final blend on the line. Circle the picture.

1. a n t ________

2. l i s t ________

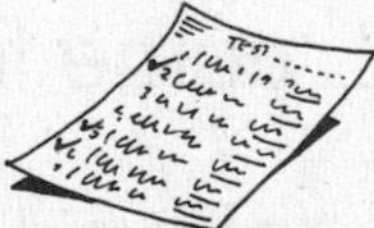

3. b a n d ________

4. r i n k ________

TEKS 1.3 (A) (iii) Decode words in isolation by applying common letter-sound correspondences, including consonant blends.

Name ______________________________

Roberto Clemente is a biography. A **biography** tells about someone's life.

Answer each question.

1. What sport did Roberto Clemente play? Write your answer.

____

2. Tell about Roberto Clemente's life. Write 1 next to what happened first. Write 2 next to what happened later. Write 3 next to what happened last.

_________ came to the United States

_________ played with friends

_________ helped children

3. Why was Roberto Clemente a hero? Draw or write your answer.

TEKS 1.14 (A) Restate the main idea, heard or read.
1.14 (B) Identify important facts or details in text, heard or read.
1.14 (C) Retell the order of events in a text by referring to the words.

Name ____________________

Use a word from the box to complete each sentence.

very	help	use	now

1. Tom can ____________ Nan ride.

2. Look! What she did is ____________ good.

3. Sam and Matt go up and down ____________.

4. Dick and Nan ____________ the big pot.

TEKS **1.3 (H)** Identify and read at least 100 high-frequency words from a commonly used list.

Name ___________________________

A B C D E F G H I J K L M N O P Q R S T U V W X Y Z

The first letter of a word tells you where to put it in ABC order.

Read each set of words. Circle the word that comes last in ABC order.

1. miss kick ran

2. pass go hit

3. jump over run fast

4. land use miss go

5. pass land hit over

TEKS 1.1 (C) Sequence the letters of the alphabet.

Name ______________________________

As you read Soccer, fill in the Author's Purpose Chart. Use words from the story.

Clue	Clue

Author's Purpose

How does the Author's Purpose Chart help you understand the topic of the story Soccer?

TEKS **1.13** Identify the topic of the text and explain the author's purpose in writing about the text.

Name ______________________________

Some authors write to tell a story. Some authors write to tell about real people or things.

Read the sentences. Think about the topic. Choose the author's purpose.

1. Nan and I like to play soccer. Nan can run fast. Nan can run as fast as the wind. Can I pass her? Nan and I zig and zag on the grass. Nan can kick the ball up. I can kick it, too. But we can not use our hands. When the ball is out, we are sad. When it lands in, we are glad!

   Author's purpose is:

   ○ tell a story about friends playing soccer

   ○ tell about real things

2. A band plays on the hill. Hank, Jim, and Dan play baseball. Nan, Pam, and I play soccer. Wag runs and jumps on the grass. Then it rains. Drip! Drip! Drip! The band packs up its van to go. We will play on another day.

   Author's purpose is:

   ○ tell about how to play soccer

   ○ tell a story

TEKS **1.13** Identify the topic of the text and explain the author's purpose in writing about the text.

Name ______________________________

The **author's purpose** is why the author writes. Sometimes authors write to tell made-up stories. Sometimes authors write to tell facts about real people or things. The **topic** is what the text is mostly about.

Read the sentences.
Fill in the circle next to the correct answer.

1. Nat the ant helps Pat the pig pick six flowers.
The author's purpose is to

○ tell a made-up story.

○ tell about real people or things.

2. Cats can sit. Cats can run. Cats can jump up and down.
The author's purpose is to

○ tell a made-up story.

○ tell about real people or things.

3. It is Fish's birthday. Crab gives Fish a gift.
Happy birthday, Fish!
The topic of this passage is

○ Crab's busy day.

○ Fish's birthday.

TEKS **1.13** Identify the topic and explain the author's purpose in writing about the text.

Name ______________________________

Words in a poem often **rhyme.** Rhyming words begin with different sounds and end with the same sound.

map **tap** **clap** **flap**

Read the poem. Write the rhyming words on the line. Circle the same sound in each word.

Where Did the Ball Go?

1. Pam can kick.
   Now she is very quick.

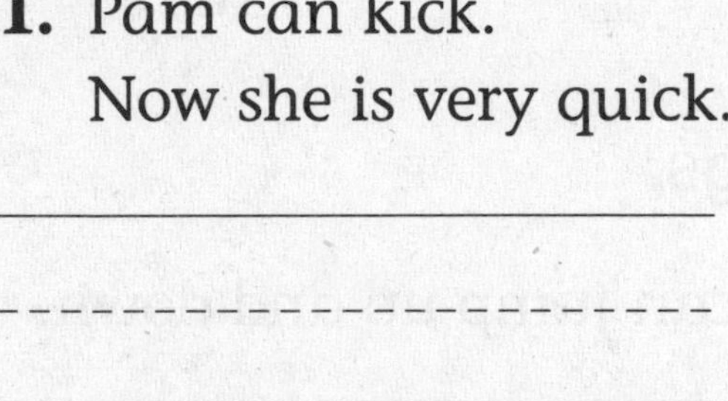

____

2. Where will the ball land?
   Will it sink in the sand?

____

Write words with *l* blends that rhyme.

Say your rhymes out loud.

____

TEKS **1.2 (A)** Orally generate a series of original rhyming words using a variety of consonant blends.
1.8 Respond to and use rhyme in poetry.

Name ______________________________

As I read, I will pay attention to pauses for sentence punctuation.

Fat Cat has a drum.
05 Fat Cat can hit it.
10 Pink Crab has a guitar.
15 Pink Crab can grab it.
20 Big Pig has a xylophone.
25 Big Pig can tap it.
30 Ant can help the band.
35 Pack Ant's van for the trip.
41 This is a jazz band!
46 Come and jig, jig, jig!
51 Ant taps and taps.
55 Ant jumps up and down.
60 Ant grins and claps.
64 The jazz band is good! 69

Comprehension Check

1. Who plays in the jazz band?

2. What can Ant do?

	Words Read	–	Number of Errors	=	Words Correct Score
First Read		–		=	
Second Read		–		=	

TEKS 1.3 (I) Monitor accuracy of decoding.
1.5 Read aloud grade-level appropriate text with fluency and comprehension.

Name ______________________________

Every sentence needs an end mark.

Sometimes the end mark is a period.

When you write a sentence, leave a space between your words.

A. Trace the capital letter at the beginning of each sentence. Then complete each sentence. Remember to leave space between your words. Include an end mark at the end of the sentence.

1. I like to ______________________________

2. At home, I help ______________________________

3. My friend is ______________________________

B. On the line, write the next letter in the alphabet. Write a capital letter.

4. J ______

5. C ______

TEKS 1.1 (D) Recognize the distinguishing features of a sentence.
1.21 (A) Form upper- and lower-case letters legibly in text, using the basic conventions of print, including spacing between words and sentences.

Name ______________________

The letter **o** stands for the middle sound in **log**.

Blend the vowel and consonant sounds and say the word. Then write the word and circle the picture.

1. p o t ____________

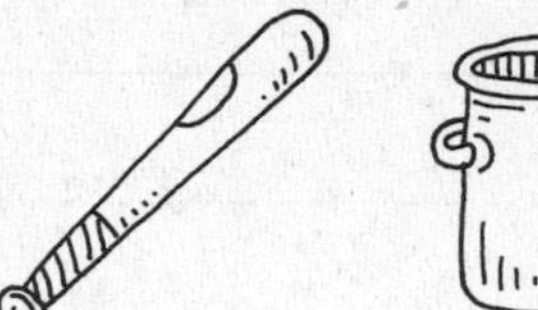  

2. h o g ____________

3. b o x ____________

  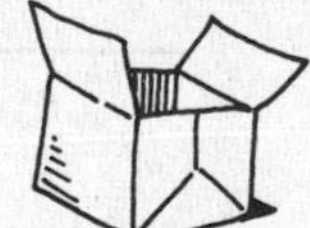

4. f o x ____________

Write two sentences using these spelling words: hop, top, hot.

Check your spelling.

TEKS **1.3 (A) (i) (ii)** Decode words in context and in isolation by applying common letter-sound correspondences, including single letters (consonants and vowels). **1.22 (B) (i)** Use letter-sound patterns to spell consonant-vowel-consonant (CVC) words.

Name ________________________________

Wild Animal Families is **nonfiction**. Nonfiction tells about real people and things.

Answer each question.

1. What is Wild Animal Families mostly about? Write your answer.

____

____

2. Tell about a wolf pup's life. Write 1 next to what happens first. Write 2 next to what happens later. Write 3 next to what happens last.

   ________ The pups get food from their parents.

   ________ New wolf pups cannot see or hear.

   ________ When they are six months old, wolf pups hunt with the pack.

3. How does a father penguin protect the egg? Write your answer.

____

____

TEKS **1.14 (A)** Restate the main idea, heard or read. **1.14 (B)** Identify important facts or details in text, heard or read. **1.14 (C)** Retell the order of events in a text, by referring to the words and/or illustrations.

Name ______________________

Write the word that completes each sentence.

Our	two	her	They

1. ______________ cat is a mom.

2. The small cat naps with ______________ mom.

3. This mom has ______________ pups.

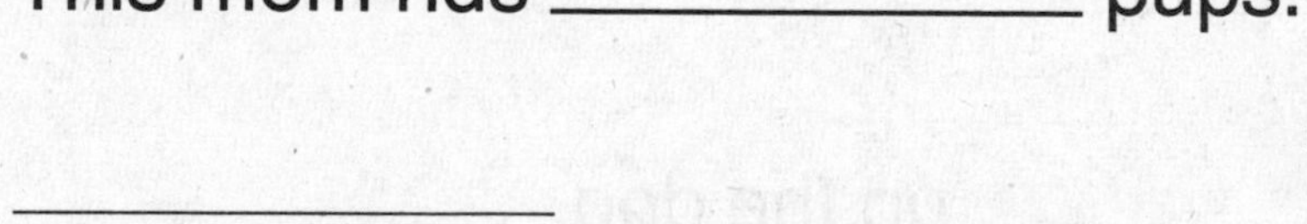

4. ______________ play with mom.

Put the words on the top of the page in ABC order. If the first letter is the same, use the second letter.

______________ ______________ ______________ ______________

TEKS 1.3 (H) Identify and read at least 100 high-frequency words from a commonly used list. 1.6 (E)(1)(2) Alphabetize a series of words to the first and second letter.

Name ___________________________

You can add **-ed** to some action words to tell what someone or something did. **walk + ed = walked**

Circle the word that completes the sentence. Write the word. Then check your spelling.

1. I ______________ my bag.

   rocked packed

2. Dad ______________ the  .

   locked packed

3. Bob ______________ up the dog.

   picked licked

4. The cat ______________ up on my lap.

   jumped picked

5. Pat ______________ the  .

   rocked kicked

TEKS 1.20 (A) (i) Understand and use past-tense verbs in the context of reading, writing, and speaking.
1.22 (D) Spell base words with inflectional endings.

Name ______________________________

As you read Animal Moms and Dads, fill in the Main Idea and Details Chart. Use words from the story.

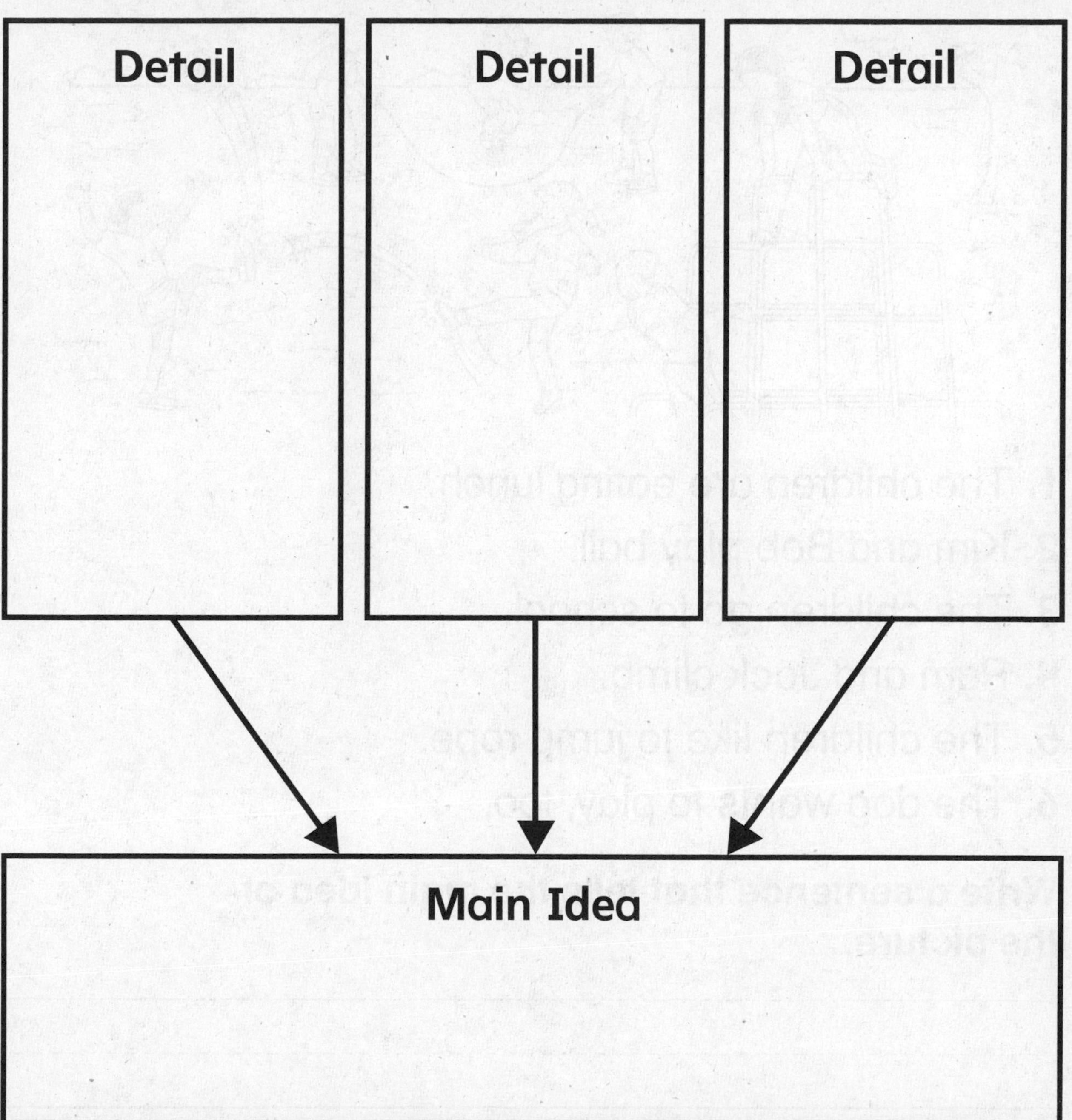

How does the Main Idea and Details Chart help you retell Animal Moms and Dads?

TEKS 1.14 (A) Restate the main idea, heard or read.
1.14 (B) Identify important facts or details in text, heard or read.

Name ______________________

Look at the picture. Circle all the sentences that tell important details about the picture.

1. The children are eating lunch.
2. Kim and Bob play ball.
3. The children go to school.
4. Pam and Jack climb.
5. The children like to jump rope.
6. The dog wants to play, too.

Write a sentence that tells the main idea of the picture.

____

____

TEKS 1.14 (A) Restate the main idea, heard or read.
1.14 (B) Identify important facts or details in text, heard or read.

Name ________________________________

Read the passage. Then complete the items.

A puppy will be a dog. Its mom will help it grow.
A kitten will be a cat. Its mom will help it grow.
A tadpole will be a frog. Its mom will help it grow.

1. Circle the main idea of this passage.

   Frogs like to sit in ponds.
   Baby animals have a mom to help them grow.

2. Circle the group of pictures that shows the order in which the animals are talked about.

3. Circle what you think a chick's mom will do. Use details from the story to help you.

   Go to the store. Help it grow.

TEKS **1.14 (A)** Restate the main idea, heard or read. **1.14 (C)** Retell the order of events in a text by referring to the words and/or illustrations. **RC-1 (D)** Make inferences about text and use textual evidence to support understanding.

Name ______________________________

Rhythm Poems are written so that the words have a certain beat when you say them aloud.

Rhyme Words that rhyme end in the same sounds.

Read the poem.

One little cat,
Sat on a mat.
She did not run,
She did not pat.

One little frog,
Sat on a log.
He did not jump,
He did not jog.

1. Write three words that rhyme in the first verse.

_______________ _______________ _______________

2. Write three words that rhyme in the second verse.

_______________ _______________ _______________

3. Say the poems out loud. Underline words that have a strong beat.

TEKS 1.8 Respond to and use rhythm and rhyme in poetry.

Name ______________________________

Practice

Fluency: Echo Read: Phrasing

As I read, I will pay attention to patterns in the story.

Mom Fox is very sad.
05 Where is Bob Fox now?
10 Is Bob Fox in Frog's pond?
16 Bob is not in Frog's pond.
22 Is Bob Fox in Tom's box?
28 Bob is not in Tom's box.
34 Mom Fox is sad.
38 Mom sits on a rock.
43 Mom can use help.
47 Ant can help Mom Fox.
52 Now Mom can see Bob Fox! 58

Comprehension Check

1. Why is Mom Fox sad?

2. Who helps Mom Fox?

	Words Read	–	Number of Errors	=	Words Correct Score
First Read		–		=	
Second Read		–		=	

TEKS **1.3 (I)** Monitor accuracy of decoding.
1.5 Read aloud grade-level appropriate text with fluency and comprehension.

Name ____________________

Practice

Concepts of Print

A **sentence** always begins with a capital letter and ends with an end mark.

The end mark can be a period or a question mark.

Read this story aloud. Then complete the items.

I like to dance. I am a star.
I can sing. I am a star.
I can jump rope. I am a star.
I like to read. I am a star.
What makes you a star?

1. Draw a box around the first word you read.
2. Find these words in the story. Circle them.

3. Underline a capital letter at the beginning of a sentence.
4. What letter follows that letter in the alphabet? ____
5. Circle the two end marks you see in the story.

TEKS 1.1 (A) Recognize that spoken words are represented in written English by specific sequences of letters. 1.1 (B) Identify upper-case letters. 1.1 (C) Sequence the letters of the alphabet. 1.1 (D) Recognize the distinguishing features of a sentence.

Name ____________________

Practice

Phonics: Short *e*

Use the words from the box to name each picture.

pen	net	hen	leg	bed	ten

1.  ____________

2.   ____________

3.  ____________

4. 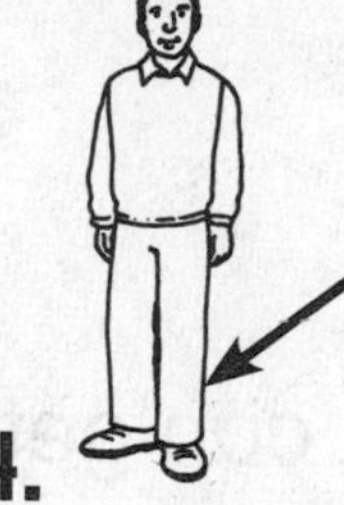 ____________

5. **10** ____________

6. ____________

Write two sentences using these spelling words: men, let, get. Check your spelling.

____

____

TEKS **1.3 (A) (i) (ii)** Decode words in context and in isolation by applying common letter-sound correspondences, including single letters (consonants and vowels).
1.22 (B) (i) Use letter-sound patterns to spell consonant-vowel-consonant (CVC) words.

Name ______________________

Practice

High-Frequency Words/Vocabulary

Write a word from the box to complete each sentence.

Who	some	of	No	eat

1. Did you get ____________  for me?

2. ____________ can get the  down?

3. The bag ____________  is in the box.

4. ____________, I can not ride a  .

5. Can I ____________ with you?

TEKS **1.3 (H)** Identify and read at least 100 high-frequency words from a commonly used list.

Name ______________________

A **contraction** is a short form of two words. An **apostrophe (')** takes the place of the missing letters. can + not = **can't**

didn't can't doesn't isn't

A. Write the contractions.

1. does not ______________

2. did not ______________

3. can not ______________

4. is not ______________

B. Write a sentence using a contraction from the box.

____

TEKS 1.3 (G) Identify and read contractions.

Name ______________________________

As you read Little Red Hen, fill in the Retelling Chart. Use words from the story.

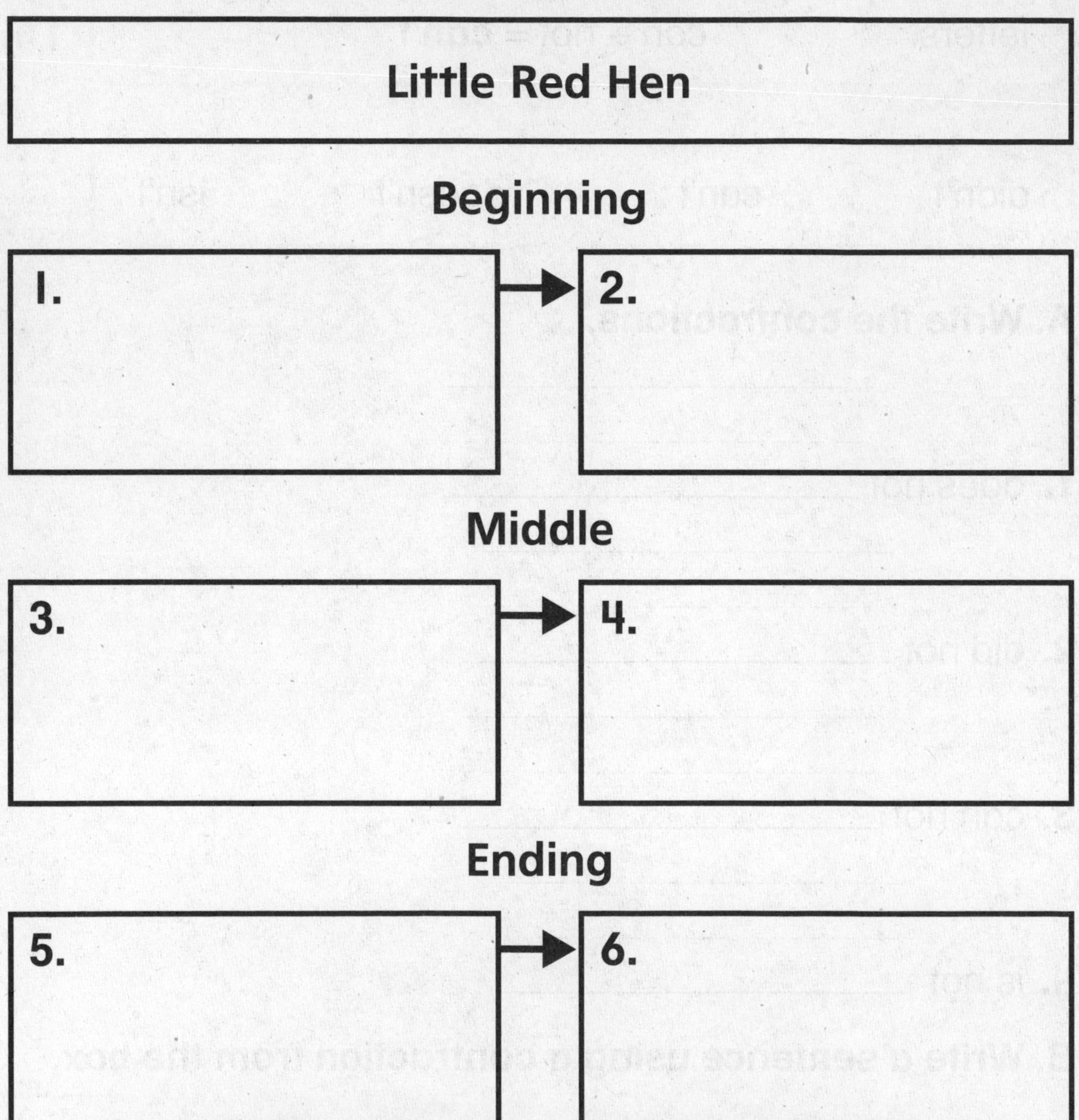

How does the Retelling Chart help you remember the beginning, middle, and ending of Little Red Hen?

TEKS **1.9 (A)** Retell a story's beginning, middle, and end with attention to the sequence of events.

Name ______________________________

When you **retell** a story, you tell what happened at the beginning, middle, and ending.

Read each story. Write a new sentence that tells the ending. Then draw a picture.

The red hen has two eggs.
She sits on the nest.
Now the eggs crack.
The chicks jump down from the nest.

1. ______________________________

Jen has a pet cat.
Greg has a pet dog.
Jen's cat jumps on Greg's dog.
The dog does not run.
Greg's dog licks Jen's cat.

2. ______________________________

TEKS 1.9 (A) Retell a story's beginning, middle, and end with attention to the sequence of events.

Name ______________________________

Read the story. Then answer the questions.

I can get my mom a gift.
I will ask my dad for help.
I will pick the best gift.
I will tell my mom, "I love you!"

1. Look at the pictures. Write 1, 2, and 3 to show the order in which things happen in the story.

 ________

 ________

 ________

2. The boy in the story has a problem. Fill in the circle that matches the boy's problem:

○ He needs help to get a gift.

○ He needs to run very fast.

3. Whom does the boy ask for help? Circle the picture.

TEKS **1.9 (A)** Describe the plot (problem and solution) and retell a story's beginning, middle, and end with attention to the sequence of events. **RC-1** (E) Retell important events in stories in logical order.

Name ________________________________

A **folktale** is a story that has been told over and over again. Folktales often have talking animals that behave just as people do.

Think about a folktale such as "The Three Little Pigs." Many folktales have the same words at the beginning and the end of the story.

1. What do the words "Once upon a time" tell you? Fill in the circle.

   ○ The story happened long ago.

   ○ The story happened yesterday.

   ○ The story happens today.

2. What do the words "They lived happily ever after" tell you? Fill in the circle.

   ○ The story is about real animals.

   ○ The story is about real people.

   ○ The story is a folktale.

3. Think about "The Little Red Hen." Write what Cat, Pig, and Dog say when Hen asks for help.

   ____

   ____

TEKS 1.7 (B) Explain the function of recurring phrases in traditional folk tales.

Name ______________________________

A **diagram** is a picture that shows the parts of something.

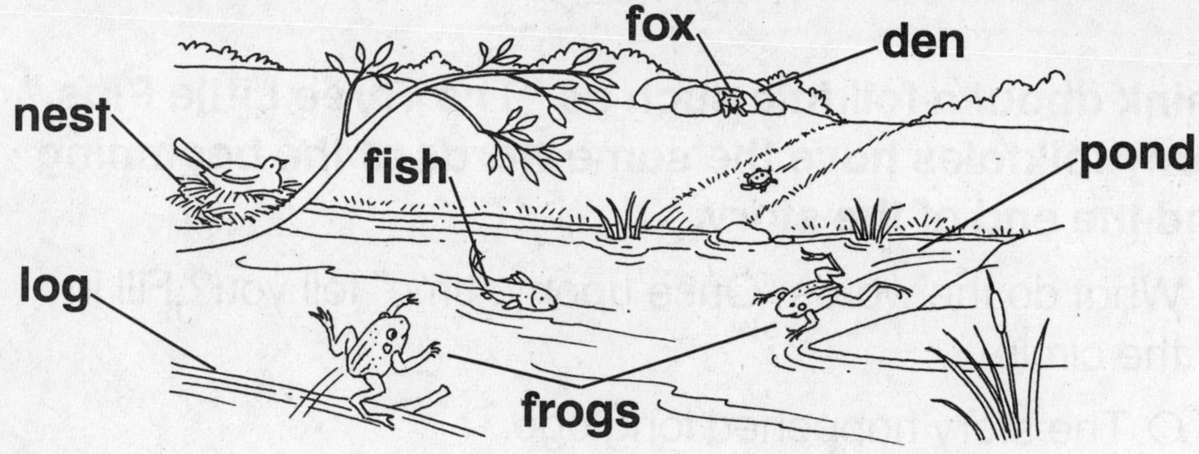

Write a word from the diagram to complete each sentence.

1. Two frogs jump in the ______________.

2. The frog jumps off of the ______________.

3. A fox is in a ______________.

4. A ______________ is in the pond.

TEKS 1.14 (D) Use text features to locate specific information in text.

Name ______________________________

Practice

Fluency: Echo Read: Expression

As I read, I will pay attention to the questions in the passage and how they affect expression.

“Ben, can Mom fix eggs?”
05 “Yes, Meg. Get two eggs.”
10 “We have one egg.
14 Get Hen’s egg, Ben.”
18 Does Hen have eggs?
22 Ben is in her pen.
27 Hen is mad!
30 Meg yells for Mom and Dad.
36 They will help.
39 Splat!
40 Mom will not fix eggs.
45 Mom will fix ham! 49

Comprehension Check

1. Where does Ben go to get eggs?

2. Who does Meg get to help?

	Words Read	–	Number of Errors	=	Words Correct Score
First Read		–		=	
Second Read		–		=	

TEKS **1.3 (I)** Monitor accuracy of decoding.
1.5 Read aloud grade-level appropriate text with fluency and comprehension.

Name ______________________

Practice

Concepts of Print

A **sentence** is a group of words that tells a whole idea. When you write a sentence, leave a space between your words. Include an end mark.

A. Circle the capital letter at the beginning of each sentence. Underline the first lowercase letter. Complete the sentence. Add an end mark.

1. My family helps me ______________________

2. Who went to ______________________

B. Write a sentence telling how you help at home. Check the space between words.

____

____

TEKS **1.1 (D)** Recognize the distinguishing features of a sentence.
1.21 (A) Form upper- and lower-case letters legibly in text, using the basic conventions of print.

Name ______________________________

Sometimes consonants form a **blend**. You can hear each consonant sound in a **consonant blend**.

Read the word. Write the word.
Circle the picture that it names.

1. g r a s s

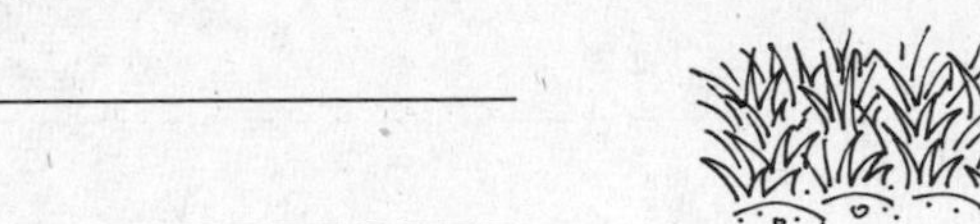

2. c r a b

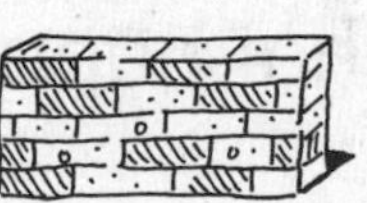

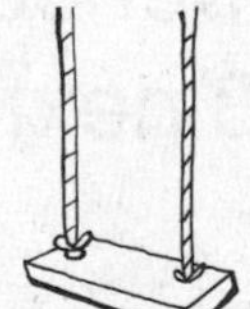

3. s n a p

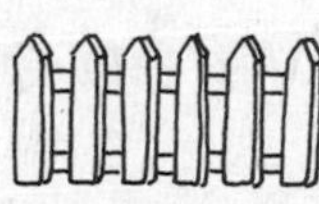

4. c r i b

Write two sentences using these spelling words: drip, spin, spill. Check your spelling.

Name ____________________

Around Town, Then and Now is **nonfiction**.
Nonfiction tells about real people and events.

Complete each item.

1. How did people travel long ago? Write your answer.

____

____

2. Tell about mail service long ago and today. Write 1 next to what happened first. Write 2 next to what happened later. Write 3 next to what happened last.

_______ A stagecoach delivered the mail.

_______ Mail is delivered by a mail carrier.

_______ Pony Express riders delivered the mail.

3. How was school long ago different from today? Write your answer.

____

____

TEKS 1.14 (A) Restate the main idea, heard or read. 1.14 (B) Identify important facts or details in text, heard or read. 1.14 (C) Retell the order of events in a text by referring to the words.

Name ______________________________

live many out place

Write the word that completes each sentence.

1. Come to our ______________.

2. We ______________ here.

3. We have ______________ pals.

4. We go ______________ to play.

Put the words on the top of the page in alphabetical order.

__________ __________ __________ __________

TEKS **1.3 (H)** Identify and read at least 100 high-frequency words from a commonly used list. **1.6 (E)(1)** Alphabetize a series of words to the first letter.

Name ______________________

Practice

Structural Analysis: Inflectional Ending *-ing*

You can add **-ing** to some action words.

A. Add -ing to the words in the box.

look ______________ jump ______________

play ______________ wash ______________

B. Complete the sentences with the words you wrote. Check your spelling.

1. Beth is ______________ a big dog.

2. They are ______________ for a lost cat.

3. I am ______________ with a little ship.

4. We are ______________ up and down.

TEKS 1.20 (A) (i) Understand and use present-tense verbs in the context of reading, writing, and speaking.
1.22 (D) Spell base words with inflectional endings.

Name ____________________

As you read On the Map!, fill in the Main Idea and Details Chart. Use words from the story.

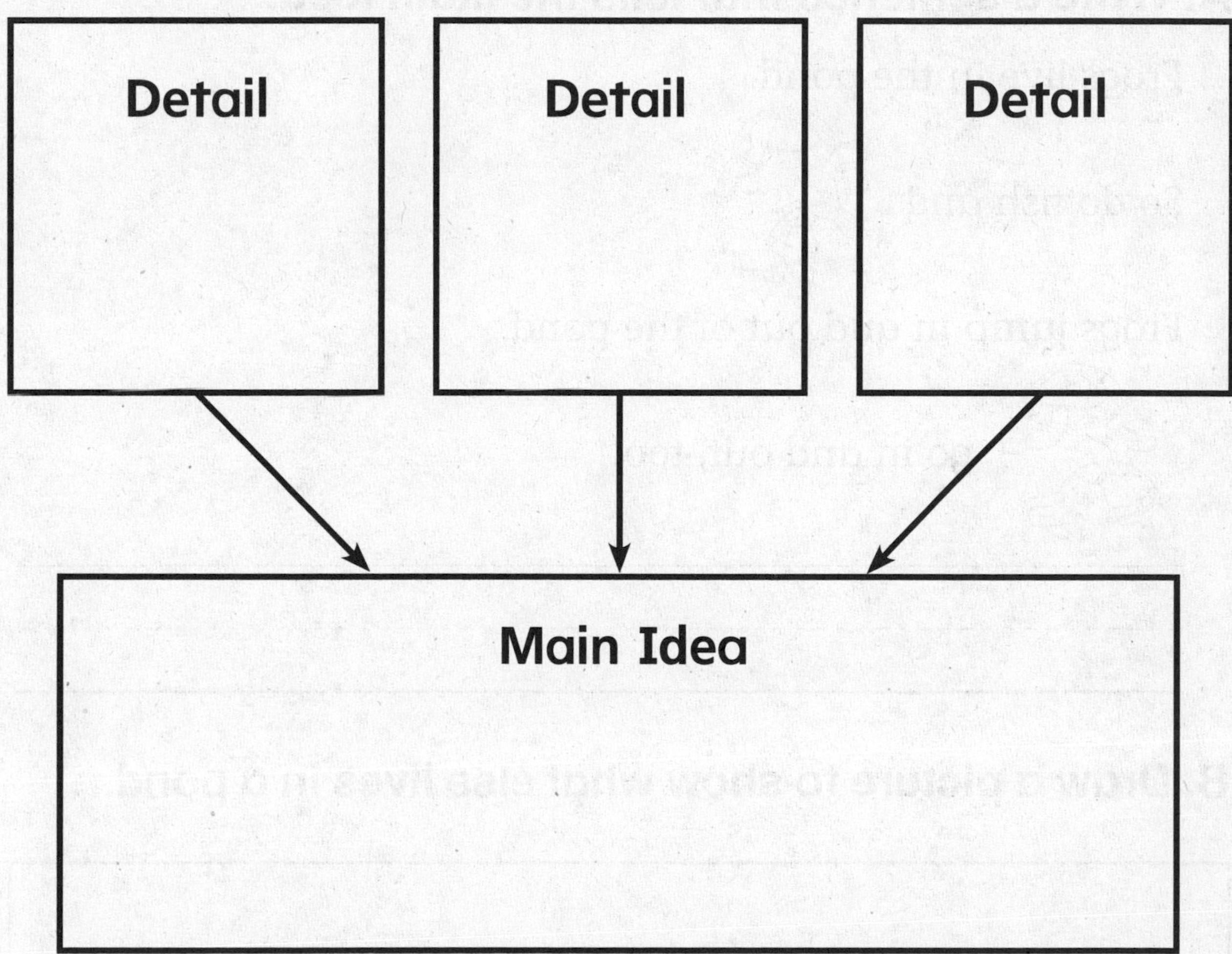

How does the information you wrote in this Main Idea and Details Chart help you retell On the Map!?

TEKS **1.14 (A)** Restate the main idea, heard or read.
1.14 (B) Identify important facts or details in text, heard or read.

Name ______________________________

Identify the **important facts and details** in a story. Then state the **main idea**.

A. Write a sentence that tells the main idea.

Frogs live in the pond.

So do fish and  .

Frogs jump in and out of the pond.

 go in and out, too.

____

B. Draw a picture to show what else lives in a pond.

TEKS 1.14 (A) Restate the main idea, heard or read.
1.14 (B) Identify important facts or details in text, heard or read.

Name ______________________________

Read the story. Then answer the questions.

I am a big black bear. I live in the woods.
Today it is hot. I stop to get a drink.
Now the leaves look red and yellow. It is not so hot. It is fall.
It is cold. It is snowy. I go to sleep.
I wake up. It is green and it is spring. I will eat a lot!

1. Look at the pictures below. Write 1, 2, 3, and 4 to show the order in which things happen in the story.

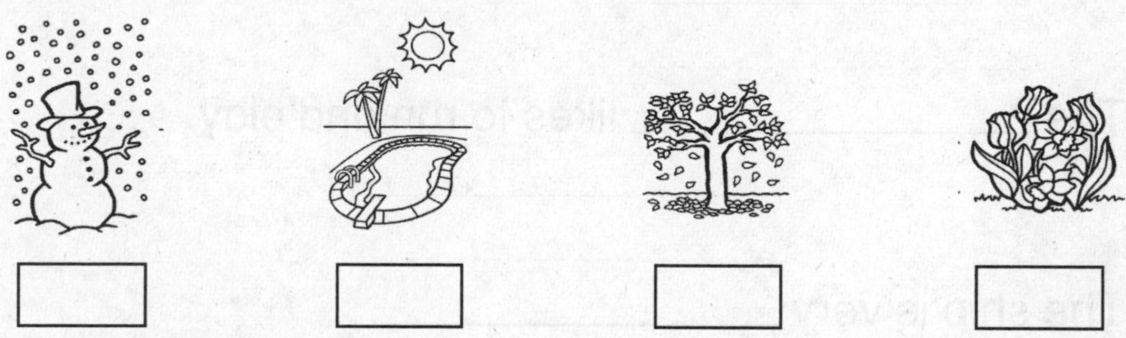

2. What is a good title for this story? Fill in the circle next to the best answer.

○ Bear Sees the Seasons

○ Bear Likes to Eat

3. Why will the bear eat a lot in spring? Fill in the circle next to the best answer.

○ He has been sleeping all winter.

○ A big apple fell next to him.

TEKS **1.13** Identify the topic of the text. **1.14 (B)** Identify important facts or details in text, heard or read. **1.14 (C)** Retell the order of events in a text by referring to the words and/or illustrations. **RC-1 (E)** Retell important events in stories in logical order.

Name ______________________

A **dictionary** gives the meaning of words.

grand very big

ship a big 

mend to fix

lamb a little 

A. Write a dictionary word to complete each sentence.

1. The ______________ likes to run and play.

2. The ship is very ______________.

3. I have to ______________ my pants.

4. A ______________ is too big for a pond.

B. Write a new sentence for one of the words.

5. ______________________________

TEKS **1.6 (E)** Use a dictionary to find words.
1.24 (B) Use text features in age-appropriate reference works to locate information.

Name ____________________

Practice

Fluency: Choral Read: Expression

As I read, I will pay attention to questions in the passage and how they affect expression.

Who can do a trick?
05 A lot of pets can!
10 Frizz has a trick.
14 Frizz can skip over a bat.
20 Ham can do some tricks.
25 Ham can run on a track.
31 Spot has a trick.
35 Spot can grab a rope.
40 Spot can spin.
43 Can Kit do a trick?
48 No, Kit can not.
52 But Kit can kiss.
56 It is a good trick! 61

Comprehension Check

1. What tricks can Frizz and Spot do?

2. What is the best pet trick?

	Words Read	–	Number of Errors	=	Words Correct Score
First Read		–		=	
Second Read		–		=	

TEKS **1.3 (I)** Monitor accuracy of decoding.
1.5 Read aloud grade-level appropriate text with fluency and comprehension.

Name ____________________

Practice

Concepts of Print

A. Look at the story.
Draw a box around the first word you should read.
Point to each word as you read the story.

I am a cat.
I can jump up.
"No, cat!
Do not jump up!" said the man in the hat.
I ran fast!

B. Find these uppercase and lowercase letters in the story, and circle them:

m s p D I t a N

C. Find these words in the story.
Draw a line under each word.

TEKS 1.1 (A) Recognize that spoken words are represented in written English by specific sequences of letters.
1.1 (B) Identify upper- and lower-case letters.

Name ______________________________

Practice

Phonics: Short *u*

The letter **u** stands for the middle sound in **bus**.

Circle the word that names each picture. Then write the word.

1. 

bun big

2. 

pot pup

3. 

ten tub

4. 

sun sad

5. 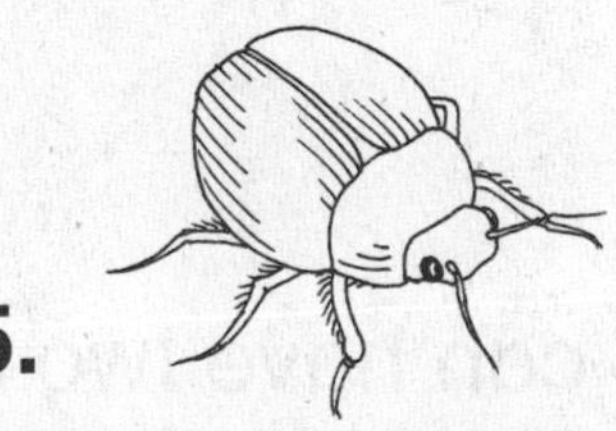

bat bug

6. 

drip drum

Write two sentences using these spelling words: run, fun, rug. Check your spelling.

TEKS **1.3 (A) (i) (ii) (iii)** Decode words in context and in isolation by applying common letter-sound correspondences, including single letters (consonants and vowels) and consonant blends. **1.22 (B) (i)** Use letter-sound patterns to spell consonant-vowel-consonant (CVC) words.

Name ______________________________

Write a word from the box to complete each sentence.

could	again	one	make	Then	three

1. I see ________________ huts.

2. I like the red ________________.

3. I ________________ live in it.

4. ________________ I can have two trees.

5. I will ________________ a swing in one.

6. I will use it again and ________________.

TEKS 1.3 (H) Identify and read at least 100 high-frequency words from a commonly used list.

Name ______________________

A **contraction** is a short form of two words. An **apostrophe** (') takes the place of one or more letters.

he's it's let's she's that's

Read each sentence. Then write the contraction for the underlined words.

1. Mom said <u>she is</u> going with us. ______________

2. <u>That is</u> a big truck! ______________

3. <u>Let us</u> run and jump. ______________

4. Ted said <u>he is</u> playing the drum. ______________

5. <u>It is</u> a dull rug. ______________

TEKS 1.3 (G) Identify and read contractions.

Name ______________________________

As you read The Pigs, the Wolf, and the Mud, fill in the Plot Chart. Use words from the story.

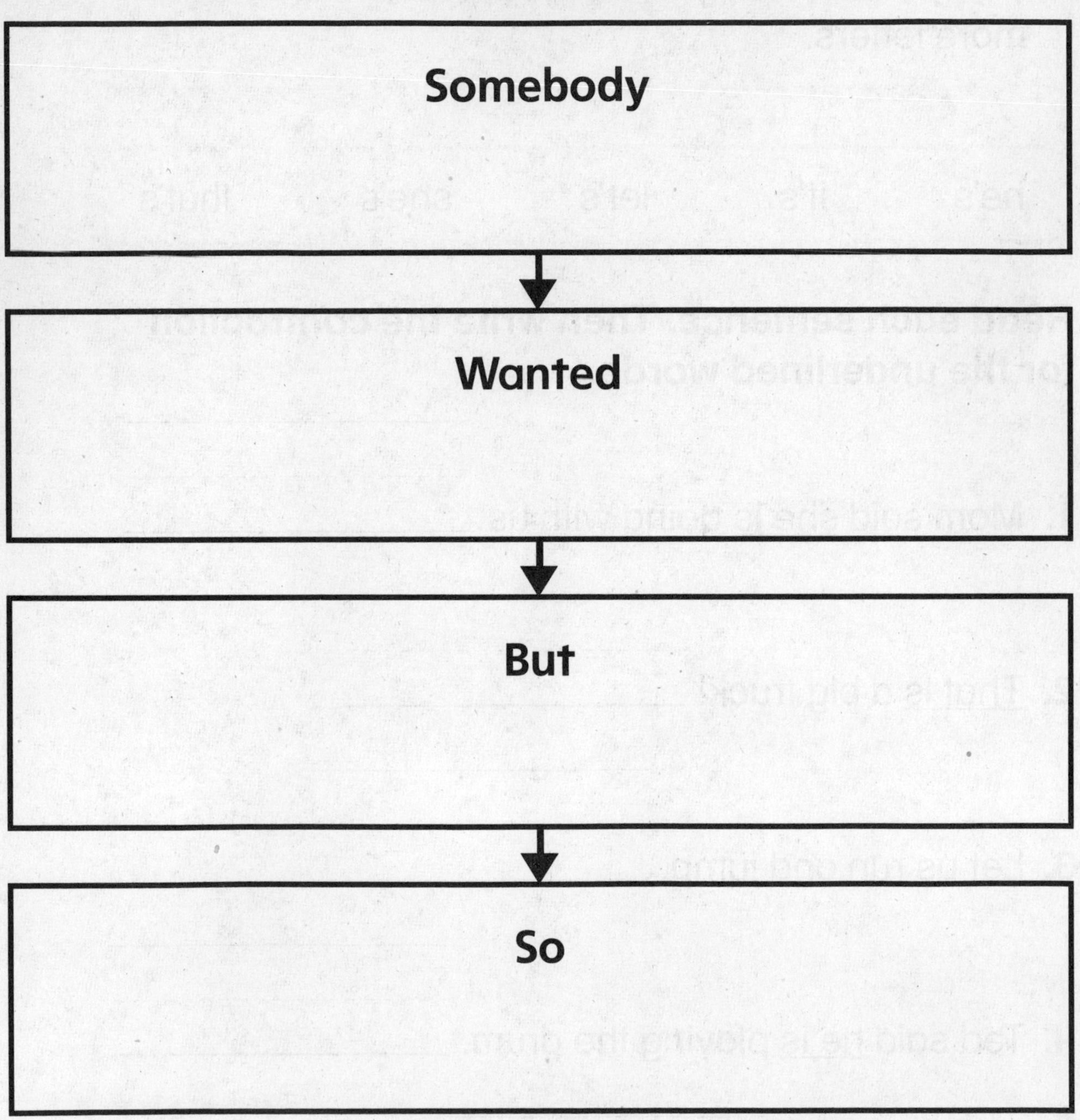

How does the Plot Chart help you better understand the problem and solution in The Pigs, the Wolf, and the Mud?

TEKS 1.9 (A) Describe the plot (problem and solution).

Name ______________________________

Read the story.

Who Could It Be?

Meg lives in a small home. Bill lives in a small home, too. Meg and Bill play. They are pals. They like to ride bikes. They like to dress up. They like to play ball.

Meg's house is too small to play in. Bill's house is too small to play in. They go out to the yard. There is more room to play. Now they can play ball, ride bikes, and have fun together.

Read the sentences. Write P for the problem. Write S for the solution.

1. Meg and Bill have fun in class. ______
2. Meg and Bill live in small homes. ______
3. There is no room to play. ______
4. Meg and Bill play outside in the yard. ______

TEKS 1.9 (A) Describe the plot and the problem and solution.

Name ______________________________

When you read, create a picture of the story in your mind. This will help you understand the story.

Read the story. Then answer the questions.

I like to run and jump in the mud.
I like to rub and scrub in the tub.
I get into bed. I am so snug.

1. Which picture shows what happens at the beginning of the story?

2. Which picture shows what happens in the middle of the story?

3. Which picture shows what happens at the end of the story?

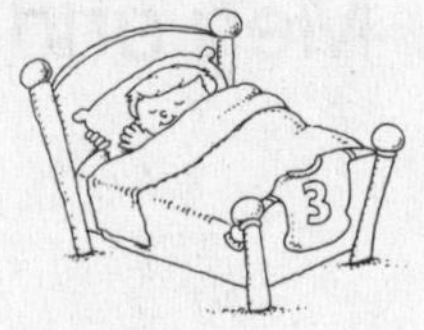

TEKS RC-1 (C) Monitor and adjust comprehension.

Name ______________________________

A **folktale** is a story that has been retold for many years. Folktales are make-believe stories. Folktales are told all over the world.

Think about the story of "*The Three Little Pigs*."

1. What does the wolf always say to the pigs? Fill in the circle.

- O "May I please come in, little pigs?"
- O "Little Pig, Little Pig, let me come in!"
- O "Hello, pigs. Will you come to my house to play?"

2. What do the pigs always say to the wolf? Fill in the circle.

- O "Well, hello kind wolf! Won't you please come on in?"
- O "No, no, no! Go away and don't ever come back!"
- O "No, no, by the hair of my chinny chin chin. I will not let you in!"

3. Suppose that there is another little pig. That little pig tells the wolf, "No, no, by the hair of my chinny chin chin. I will not let you in!" What do you think the wolf would say next?

- O "O.K., friendly pig. I will go away and leave you alone."
- O "Then I'll huff, and I'll puff, and I'll blow your house down!"
- O "Please? I am a good wolf. I will not eat you!"

TEKS **1.7 (B)** Explain the function of recurring phrases in traditional folk tales.

Photographs are pictures that show people, animals, and things in real life.

Look at the picture.

We will have a big place to live!

Write your own sentence about the picture.

Name ____________________

As I read, I will pay attention to phrasing in the story.

Gus and Fluff live in a fun place.
08 It has many nuts.
12 Gus and Fluff sit on nuts.
18 Gus and Fluff set nuts up.
24 Gus and Fluff eat nuts.
29 "Let us go out," said Gus.
35 "Yes," said Fluff.
38 "Let us get nuts!" 42

Comprehension Check

1. What do Gus have a lot of?

2. What do Gus and Fluff do with the nuts?

	Words Read	–	Number of Errors	=	Words Correct Score
First Read		–		=	
Second Read		–		=	

TEKS 1.3 (I) Monitor accuracy of decoding.
1.5 Read aloud grade-level appropriate text with fluency and comprehension.

Name ______________________

The **title** is the name of the book.

The **author** is the person who wrote the book.

The **illustrator** is the person who made the pictures.

A. Look at the book cover. Answer the questions.

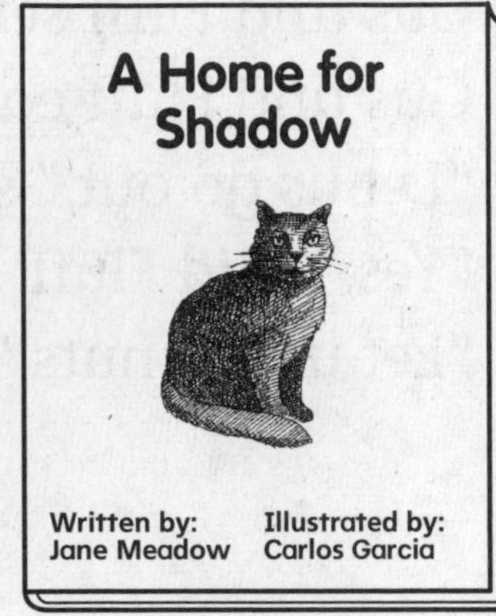

1. What is the title of this book?

____

2. Who wrote this book? ______________________

B. Complete this sentence about an animal's home. Leave space between the words. Include an end mark at the end of the sentence.

3. A frog lives ______________________

TEKS **1.1 (D)** Recognize the distinguishing features of a sentence.
1.21 (A) Form upper- and lower-case letters legibly in text, using the basic conventions of print, including spacing between words and sentences.

Name ____________________

Practice

Phonics: Digraphs *th*, *sh*, *-ng*

Read each word. Listen to the sounds that **sh**, **th**, and **ng** stand for.

pa**th** **th**ink **sh**ip swi**ng** di**sh** ba**th**

Use the words in the box to name each picture. Then circle the letters that stand for the sounds sh, th, or ng.

1.  ____________________

2.  ____________________

3. 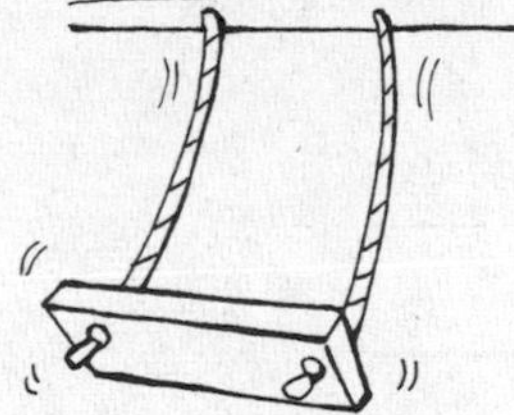 ____________________

4.  ____________________

5.  ____________________

TEKS 1.3 (A) (i) (ii) (iii) (iv) Decode words in isolation by applying common letter-sound correspondences, including single letters (consonants and vowels), consonant blends, and consonant digraphs.

Practice

High-Frequency Words/Vocabulary

Name ______________________

Write a word from the box to complete each sentence.

all	want	under	Put	show	together

1. ______________ on a hat.

2. Sit ______________ the tent.

3. Come see the ______________!

4. The kids play in a band ______________.

5. You will ______________ to see it.

6. I like ______________ the songs they play.

TEKS 1.3 (H) Identify and read at least 100 high-frequency words from a commonly used list.

Name ______________________________

A **compound word** is made up of two small words.

rose + bush = **rosebush**

back + yard = **backyard**

Match a word on the left to a word on the right to make a compound word. Then write the word.

1. bath — hill — ______________

2. down — one — ______________

3. any — care — ______________

4. day — robe — ______________

Use a compound word in a sentence.

5. ______________________________

TEKS **1.3 (F)** Use knowledge of the meaning of base words to identify common compound words. **1.6 (B)** Determine the meaning of compound words using knowledge of the meaning of their individual component words.

Name ______________________________

Practice

Comprehension: Retelling Chart

As you read Beth and the Band, fill in the Retelling Chart. Use words from the story.

Beth and the Band

Beginning

1.	→	2.

Middle

3.	→	4.

End

5.	→	6.

How does the Retelling Chart help you visualize what happens in the beginning, middle, and end of Beth and the Band?

TEKS 1.9 (A) Retell a story's beginning, middle, and end with attention to the sequence of events.

Name ________________________________

When you **retell** a story, you tell the beginning, middle, and ending.

Read the story.

Ben wants to use his fishing rod. Ben sits down at the pond with his fishing rod. Ben sits and sits. Ben sees a frog. Ben sees a bug. At last Ben gets a fish!

Draw three pictures to retell the story. Show the beginning, middle, and ending.

TEKS **1.9 (A)** Retell a story's beginning, middle, and end with attention to the sequence of events.

Name ______________________________

Visualizing is forming pictures in your mind. Visualizing helps you understand a story better.

Read the story.

I am not very big.
I have six legs.
I have three eyes.
I have two long tails.
I like to eat things that are red.
I live under a rock.

What do I look like? Draw a picture below.

Read the story again. Look at your picture. Fix things in your picture that do not match the story.

TEKS RC-1 (C) Monitor and adjust comprehension.

Name ______________________________

Historical fiction is a story set in the past. It is a story about something that did not really happen.

Long ago, a kind man lived by a river. He liked to bring treats to the fish. One night, the man could not sleep. He lit a candle. He went to the river to think. "I wish I could sleep," he said. As soon as he said this, a fish stuck its head up. The fish said, "You have left treats for me. I will help you." The fish sang until the man fell asleep.

1. What is the man's problem? Fill in the circle.

   ○ He can't find his candle. ○ He can't sleep.

2. Write one word to describe the man.

   ____

3. Retell the story. Write 1, 2, and 3 in the boxes to show the order in which things happen in the story.

   A fish sang the man to sleep. ☐

   The kind man took treats to the fish. ☐

   The man lit a candle. ☐

4. Write about a time you were kind to another person.

   ____

TEKS **1.7 (A)** Connect the meaning of a well-known story to personal experiences. **1.9 (A)** Describe the plot (problem and solution) and retell a story's beginning, middle, and end with attention to the sequence of events. **1.9 (B)** Describe characters in a story.

Name ______________________

Directions are the steps that you follow to make or do something.

Make a Fun Box

1. Get an egg carton.

2. Cut the top.

3. Give it a fun look.

4. Put in stuff.

1. What will you make? ______________________

2. What will you use? ______________________

3. What will you do with the top? ______________________

4. What will you do last? ______________________

TEKS 1.15 (A) Follow written multi-step directions with picture cues to assist with understanding.

Name ________________________________

Practice

Fluency: Choral Read: Expression

As I read, I will pay attention to the expression.

Seth had a red can.
05 What could Seth make?
09 Thump, thump, thump!
12 Tim had a red lid.
17 Thud, thud, thud!
20 Beth had a flat dish.
25 Crash, crash, crash!
28 "Again!" Seth said.
31 One, two, three!
34 Thump, thud, crash!
37 Think of things to hit.
42 Then hit this and that.
47 Thump, thud, crash! 50

Comprehension Check

1. What sounds do Seth, Tim, and Beth make?

2. What do Seth, Tim, and Beth use to make sounds?

	Words Read	–	Number of Errors	=	Words Correct Score
First Read		–		=	
Second Read		–		=	

TEKS **1.3 (I)** Monitor accuracy of decoding.
1.5 Read aloud grade-level appropriate text with fluency and comprehension.

Name ______________________________

A. Read the story aloud. Complete the items.

I can do it. I will not quit.
I can pick six apples. I can run very fast.
I can jump. I did it!
Now I will make a pie. Yum!

1. Draw a box around the first word you read.
2. Find these letters in the story. Circle them.

c I q N p a Y

3. Find these words in the story. Draw a line under them.

B. On the line write the next letter in the alphabet. Write a lowercase letter.

4. d ______________ 5. h ______________

TEKS 1.1 (A) Recognize that spoken words are represented in written English by specific sequences of letters. 1.1 (B) Identify upper- and lower-case letters. 1.1 (C) Sequence the letters of the alphabet.

Name ______________________________

Look at the word **gate**. The letters **a** and **e** stand for the **long a** sound you hear.

g **a** t e

Circle the word that names the picture. Write the word on the line.

1. 

cap cape

____

2. 

tape tap

____

3. 

pane pan

____

4. 

man mane

____

5. 

rat rate

____

6. 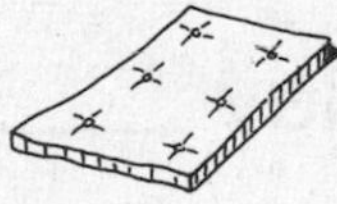

mate mat

____

TEKS **1.3 (A) (i) (ii)** Decode words in isolation by applying common letter-sound correspondences, including single letters (consonants and vowels).

Name ___________________________

Read each sentence. Write a word from the box to complete the sentence.

away	school	today	way	Why

1. ______________ did the bus go in the mud?

2. This is the ______________ to play.

3. We put the blocks ______________.

4. I have to go to ______________ now.

5. We can not play ______________.

TEKS 1.3 (H) Identify and read at least 100 high-frequency words from a commonly used list.

Name ______________________________

Look at the word: **wave**

Notice that the **e** is dropped when adding **-ing** or **-ed**.

wav**e** + **ing** = wav**ing** wav**e** + **ed** = wav**ed**

Listen for the two syllables in waving and in some of the words you will make.

Add -ing to the words. Write the new word.

1. fake ______________________

2. rake ______________________

Add -ed to the words. Write the new word.

3. bake ______________________

4. fade ______________________

5. wade ______________________

TEKS 1.3 (E) Read base words with inflectional endings.

Name ______________________________

Practice

Comprehension: Retelling Chart

As you read On My Way to School, fill in the Retelling Chart.

1.
↓
2.
↓
3.
↓
4.

How does the Retelling Chart help you remember the beginning, middle, and end of On My Way to School?

TEKS **1.9 (A)** Retell a story's beginning, middle, and end with attention to the sequence of events.

Name ________________________

Practice

Comprehension: Retell

Look at the pictures. Write what happens in each picture.

1. First, ________________________

Next, ________________________

Last, ________________________

2.

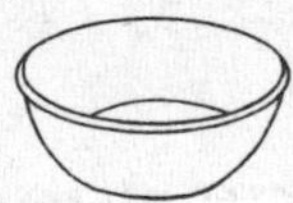

First, ________________________

Next, ________________________

Last, ________________________

TEKS **1.14 (C)** Retell the order of events in a text by referring to the illustrations.
1.14 (D) Use text features to locate specific information in text.

Name ____________________

In some stories the words **rhyme**. They have the same end sound. Sometimes the words begin with the same sound. This is called **alliteration**.

Read the rhyming story. Then complete the items.

I am a hen, and I say, "Cluck!"
I like to play with my friend, Duck.

Duck likes water, but I do not.
We both like the beaks that we've got!

We snap and snack on grass and bugs.
We like to share a lot of hugs.

I like Duck, and she likes me.
We live together happily.

1. Circle the words in the poem that rhyme.
2. Underline the word that begins the same way as *snap*.
3. Write to tell what you liked most about this rhyming story.

____

____

TEKS **1.8** Respond to and use rhyme and alliteration in poetry.
1.19 (C) Write brief comments on literary texts.

Name ______________________________

A rhyming story is like a poem. The rhyming words create a rhythm that makes the story fun to read.

I am not fast. I'm very slow.
I creep and crawl wherever I go.
I have a shell upon my back.
I eat some leaves if I want a snack.
I make a shiny, slimy trail.
Who am I? I am a ____________.

1. Finish the story. Circle the picture that makes sense and rhymes.

2. Write a poem. Write about two things that you can see.

____

____

____

TEKS 1.8 Respond to and use rhythm and rhyme in poetry.
1.18 (B) Write short poems that convey sensory details.

Name ____________________

Practice

Text Feature: Signs and Symbols

A **sign** uses words or pictures to tell you what to do.

Circle the word that completes each sentence.

1. When you see 

, you _____.

stop go

2. When you see , you _____.

stop go

3. When we go to the , we play on the _____.

beds swings

4. We _____ in the .

run eat

Color the traffic light with red, yellow, and green.
Put a ✔ next to the color that tells you to go.
Put an X next to the color that tells you to stop.

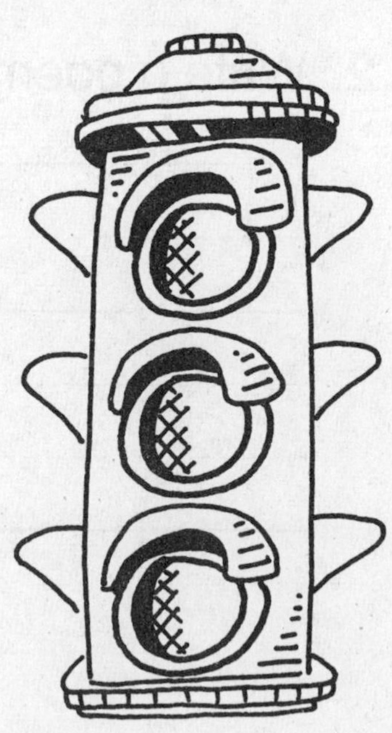

TEKS 1.15 (B) Explain the meaning of specific signs and symbols.

Name ______________________________

Practice

Fluency: Echo Read: Expression

As I read, I will pay attention to my expression.

We gave a pet show. It was
07 at the Tate School in Miss Hale's
14 class. Gale came with pet fish.
20 Shane came with his dog.
25 Dave came with a snake!
30 Jane came with a frog.
35 "His name is Wade," said Jane.
41 "Wade is the best pet."
46 "Why?" Gale asked.
49 Just then Wade jumped up.
54 Jane yelled, "Get Wade!"
58 We all helped together.
62 But Jane's frog got away!
67 Where did Wade end up?
72 He jumped in the fish tank! 78

Comprehension Check

1. What did Miss Hale's class do?

2. What did Wade do?

	Words Read	–	Number of Errors	=	Words Correct Score
First Read		–		=	
Second Read		–		=	

TEKS **1.3 (I)** Monitor accuracy of decoding.
1.5 Read aloud grade-level appropriate text with fluency and comprehension.

Name ______________________________

The cover tells the **title**, or name, of the book. It tells the name of the **author**, or person who wrote the book. The cover also tells the **illustrator**, or person who made the pictures.

A. Look at the book cover. Then answer the questions.

1. Draw a circle around the title of the book.
2. Draw a box around the name of the author.
3. Underline the name of the illustrator.

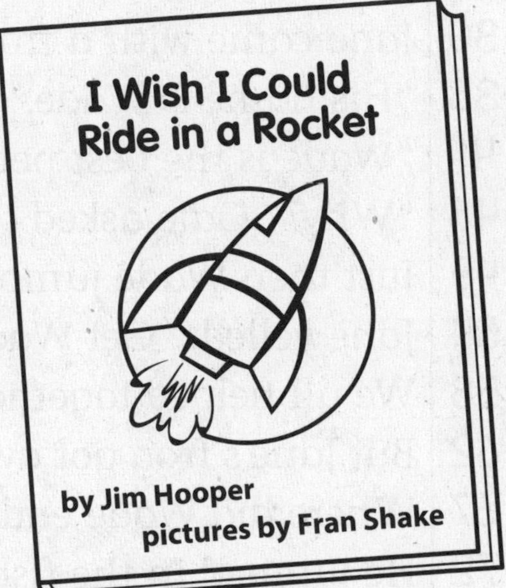

B. Write two sentences about a book that you like. Check that you leave space between your words.

____

____

TEKS **1.1 (F)** Identify the information that different parts of a book provide.
1.21 (A) Form upper- and lower-case letters legibly in text, using the basic conventions of print, including spacing between words and sentences.

Practice

Phonics: Long *i: i_e*

Name ______________________

Use the words in the box to complete the sentences.

hike	time	five	bite	bike

1. Matt races very fast on his ____________.

2. What ____________ is it?

3. I see the number ____________.

4. Dan takes a big ____________ of his cake.

5. We can ____________ up this hill.

TEKS 1.3 (A) (i) (ii) Decode words in context by applying common letter-sound correspondences, including single letters (consonants and vowels).

Name ______________________________

A **tale** is a story that has been told over and over again.

Think about Now Things Are Worse. Then complete each item.

1. How did Sam and Sara feel? Why?

____

____

2. Circle the words in this list that tell what animals do.

bread	moo
cottage	bleat
cluck	bake

3. What was the wise man's final piece of advice? Draw or write your answer.

TEKS **1.6 (D)** Identify and sort words into conceptual categories. **1.9 (A)** Describe the plot (problem and solution). **1.9 (B)** Describe characters in a story and the reasons for their actions and feelings.

Name ____________________

Use the words from the box to complete the story.

call	How	more	funny	There	so

Look! ____________ is a pet show today.

I will ____________ my dog Max.

____________ many pets will be in the show today?

Will they like Max ____________ than the other pets in line?

We like to watch some of the ____________ dogs and cats.

My dog Max is ____________ good!

TEKS 1.3 (H) Identify and read at least 100 high-frequency words from a commonly used list.

Name ______________________________

The <u>c</u> in **cent** stands for the **/s/** sound. This is **soft <u>c</u>**.

The <u>g</u> in **gem** stands for the **/j/** sound. This is **soft <u>g</u>**.

The <u>dge</u> in **ledge** stands for the **/j/** sound. This is **soft <u>g</u>**.

Choose a word from the box to complete each sentence. Write it on the line. Then circle each word that has the soft <u>c</u> sound.

race	fence	edge	cage
age	nice	stage	ice

1. This box has a sharp ______________.

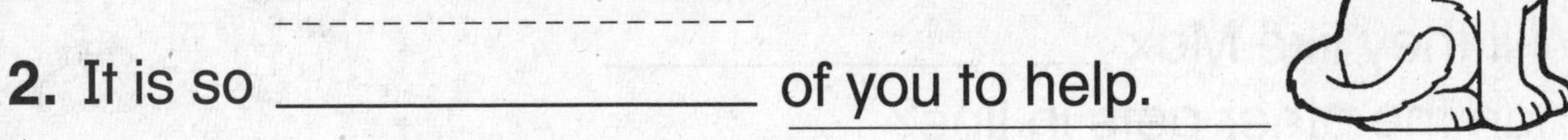

2. It is so ______________ of you to help.

3. My pet mice are out of the ______________!

4. I want to win the ______________.

5. We will stand on the ______________ to sing.

TEKS 1.3 (A) (i) (iv) Decode words in context and in isolation by applying common letter-sound correspondences, including single letters (consonant) and consonant digraphs.

Name ______________________________

Practice

Comprehension: Predictions Chart

As you read Smile, Mike!, fill in the Predictions Chart.

What I Predict	What Happens

How does the Predictions Chart help you understand what happens in Smile, Mike!?

TEKS **1.4 (A)** Confirm predictions about what will happen next in text by "reading the part that tells."

Name ____________________

Practice

Comprehension: Make Predictions

Read the sentences. Make a prediction. Read the words that tell what happens next. Check your prediction.

1. Tim's kite is ripped. Dad has some tape.

I predict that ____________________

Dad fixed Tim's kite.

Was my prediction right? Circle: Yes No

2. Sam wants a nice pup. Mom and Sam go to see the pups.

I predict that ____________________

Mom and Sam got a pup.

Was my prediction right? Circle: Yes No

TEKS 1.4 (A) Confirm predictions about what will happen next by in text by "reading the part that tells."

Name ______________________________

Read the story. Then complete the items.

I came home from school. My mom gave me a rake. I wanted to play with Nate and Pam. I did not want to rake! I raked and I raked, but the leaves kept falling! At last, I had a big pile. Then Nate and Pam came to play.

1. How do you think the boy felt when he had to rake. Why?

____

____

2. Write 1, 2, and 3 to put the events of the story in order.

______ Mom gave me a rake.

______ Nate and Pam came over to play.

______ I raked and I raked.

3. What do you think the boy, Nate, and Pam will do next?

____

TEKS **1.9 (A)** Retell a story's beginning, middle, and end with attention to the sequence of events. **1.9 (B)** Describe characters in a story and the reasons for their actions and feelings. **RC-1 (D)** Make inferences about texts.

Name ______________________________

Read the chart.

Tim's Pets	Nan's Pets
cats 3	cat 2
mice 5	mice 2
dog 1	dogs 2
fish 9	fish 10

Count the pets and then complete the sentences.

1. Tim has ______________ fish.

2. Nan has ______________ mice.

3. Tim has ______________ dog.

4. Nan has ______________ fish.

TEKS 1.14 (D) Use text features to locate specific information in text.

Name ______________________________

Practice

Fluency: Echo Read: Expression

As I read, I will pay attention to the expression.

Mom and Dad rest today.
5 "Let's switch our jobs," Mike and Kim tell them.
14 "Fine," nod Mom and Dad.
19 "Would you like a snack?" Mike asks Dad.
27 Dad takes a bite. "This is not ripe! Take it away!"
38 Mom rides Kim's bike. "Your bike isn't my size,"
47 Mom tells Kim. "It is way too little!"
55 Dad must make Mike's bed.
60 "Let's make it line up," Dad tells Mike.
68 But Dad bumps the light.
73 Kim wipes up the suds. "I must rest," she whines.
83 "It's time to switch back," smiles Mom. 90

Comprehension Check

1. What does Mike do for Dad?

2. What does Kim want to do at the end of the story?

	Words Read	–	Number of Errors	=	Words Correct Score
First Read		–		=	
Second Read		–		=	

TEKS 1.3 (I) Monitor accuracy of decoding.
1.5 Read aloud grade-level appropriate text with fluency and comprehension.

Name ______________________________

A. Circle the uppercase letters. Underline the lowercase letters. Say the letters as you read them.

e	E	j	Y	z	W	v
V	y	G	g	J	Z	w

B. Follow the letters of the alphabet in the correct order to connect the dots and make a picture.

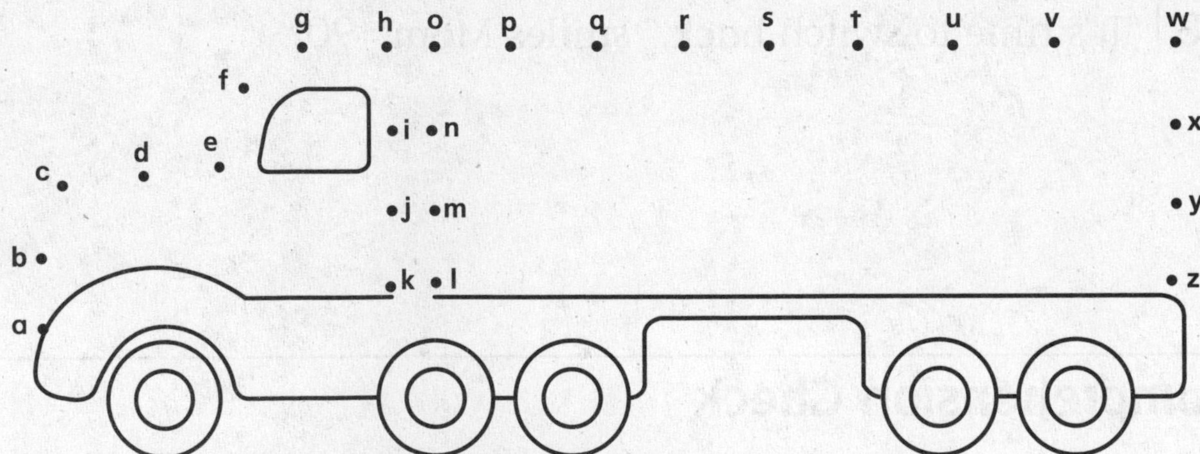

TEKS 1.1 (B) Identify upper- and lower-case letters.
1.1 (C) Sequence the letters of the alphabet.

Name ____________________

Practice

Phonics: Digraphs: *ch, tch, wh, ph*

The letters **ch** and **tch** stand for the sounds you hear in **ch**in and di**tch**.

The letters **wh** stand for the sound you hear in **wh**en.

The letters **ph** stand for the sound you hear in gra**ph**.

Choose from the letters ch, tch, wh, and ph to complete each word. Write the letters on the line.

1. ______ ase

2. lun ______

3. ______ ale

4. ______ one

5. ca ______

6. al ______ abet

TEKS 1.3 (A) (iv) Decode words in isolation by applying common letter-sound correspondences, including consonant digraphs.

Name ______________________________

Match each sentence to the picture that it explains.

1. Is this **your** brush? a. 

2. Put the dolls **into** the box. b. 

3. The **people** sing the song. c. 

4. We will make a kite **soon**. d. 

5. **Every** sock has dots. e. 

6. The gift is **from** Mom. f. 

TEKS 1.3 (H) Identify and read at least 100 high-frequency words from a commonly used list.

Name ______________________________

You can add **-s** or **-es** to name more than one person or thing.

Circle the word in each group that names more than one. Write it on the line.

1. watch watches what ______________

2. inches pitch inch ______________

3. such lunch lunches ______________

4. catch patches patch ______________

5. kisses miss kiss ______________

6. less dresses dress ______________

TEKS 1.3 (E) Read base words with inflectional endings.

Name ______________________________

As you read Masks! Masks! Masks!, fill in the Main Idea and Details Chart. Use words from the selection.

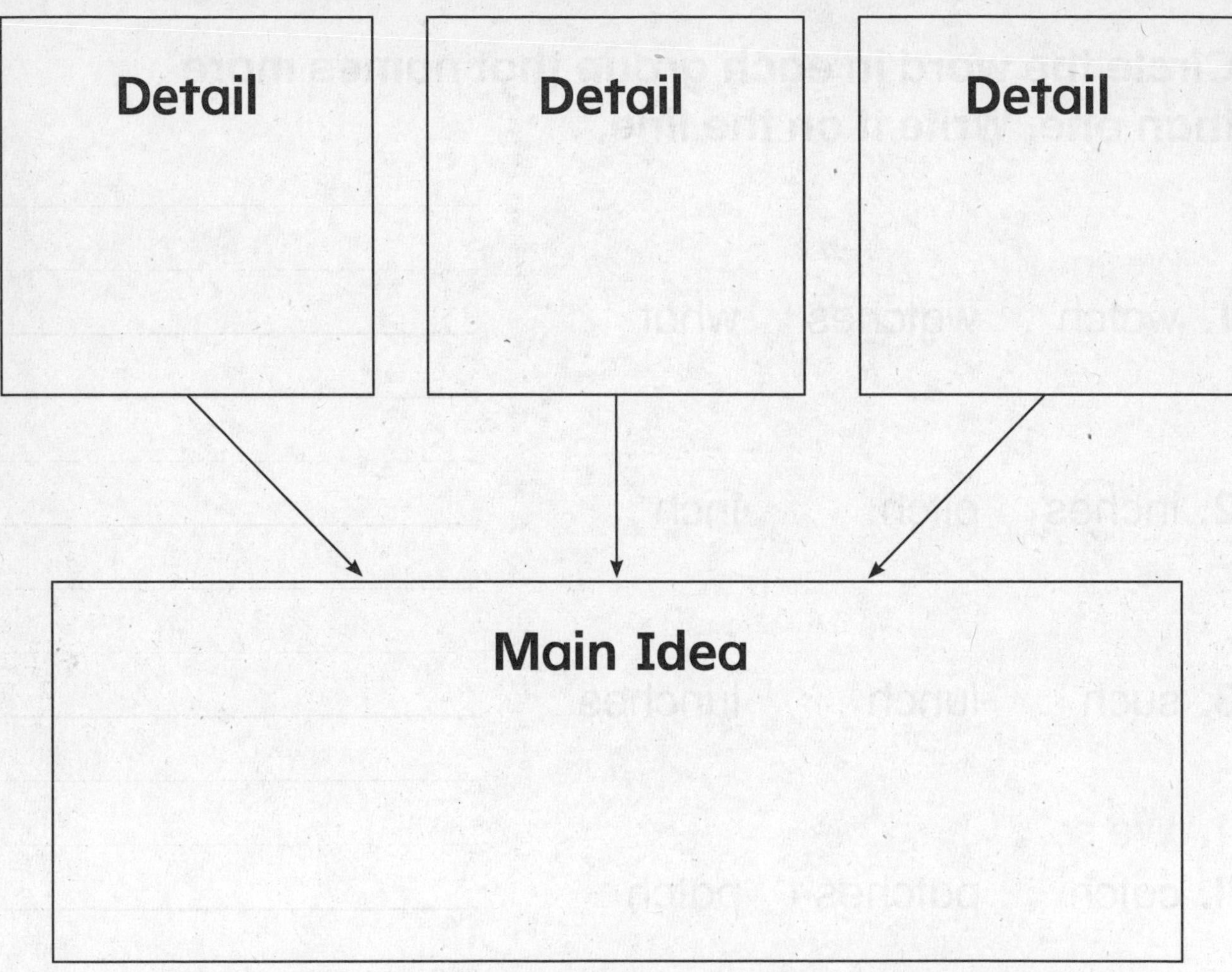

How does the information you wrote in this Main Idea and Details Chart help you retell Masks! Masks! Masks!?

TEKS 1.14 (A) Restate the main idea heard or read.
1.14 (B) Identify important facts or details in text heard or read.

Name ________________________

Details are small pieces of information in a story.
The **main idea** is the most important idea in the story.

A. Read this story.

We went out.

We sat in the sun.

We ate lunch.

The sun went down.

It was a fun day!

B. Write M if the sentence tells the main idea. Write D if it tells a detail.

1. We sat in the sun. ______

2. The sun went down. ______

3. We ate lunch. ______

4. It was a fun day! ______

TEKS 1.14 (A) Restate the main idea heard or read.
1.14 (B) Identify important facts or details in text heard or read.

Name ______________________________

Practice
Comprehension: Monitor Comprehension/ Reread

Good readers think about the story as they read. If they do not understand something in the story, they go back and read it again. This is called rereading.

Read the story. Then answer the questions.

I get my brushes and paints.
I use red, white, and black.
I add more paint.
Soon people will come to my show.

1. What does "I use red, white, and black," mean? Reread the story to look for clues. Circle the picture that matches.

2. What kind of show do you think the story is talking about? Reread the story to look for clues.

____

____

3. What kind of art do you like to make?

____

____

TEKS **1.4 (C)** Monitor comprehension, making corrections and adjustments when that understanding breaks down. **RC-1 (C)** Monitor and adjust comprehension. **RC-1 (F)** Make connections to own experiences.

Name ______________________________

Nonfiction tells about real people, places, or things. It gives facts and information. Think about the **main idea**, or what the text is mostly about, as you read. **Details** give you more information and help you find the main idea.

Read the passage. Then complete the items.

Dogs can be good pets.
You have to take care of them.
You must walk them every day.
You must give them food to eat.
You must play with them and love them a lot!

1. Underline two details in the passage.

2. What is the main idea of the passage?

____

____

____

TEKS **1.14 (A)** Restate the main idea, heard or read.
1.14 (B) Identify important facts or details in text, heard or read.

Name ______________________________

The **title** of a magazine is on the cover.
There are **articles** inside the magazine.

Use the magazine cover and article to answer the questions.

1. What is the title of the magazine?

____

2. What is on the cover?

____

3. What is the title of the article?

____

4. What could the article be about?

____

TEKS 1.14 (D) Use text features to locate specific information in text.

Name ______________________________

As I read, I will pay attention to question marks.

The big sun is up at six.
7 People stretch in bed and then get up.
15 Let's check in with them.
20 Whip up a batch of buns.
26 I wish I had a hot baked bun. Yum!
35 Which one can I pick?
40 Kids can take care of a pet.
47 This dog gets some more fresh water.
54 When will the dog get fed?
60 Kids chat in a bunch. There is a lot to tell.
71 Did you make a graph in math? Don't be late for class!
83 Kids check the lunch case.
88 Munch on fish and chips! Grab grapes and a sandwich!
98 Play a game of chess. Pitch and catch a ball.
108 The sun sets in the west. I can see pink and red.
120 I had so much fun today! 126

Comprehension Check

1. When is the big sun up?

2. How does a kid take care of a dog?

	Words Read	–	Number of Errors	=	Words Correct Score
First Read		–		=	
Second Read		–		=	

TEKS 1.3 (I) Monitor accuracy of decoding.
1.5 Read aloud grade-level appropriate text with fluency and comprehension.

Name ______________________

The cover tells the **title**, or name, of the book. It tells the name of the **author**, or person who wrote the book. The cover also tells the **illustrator**, or person who made the pictures.

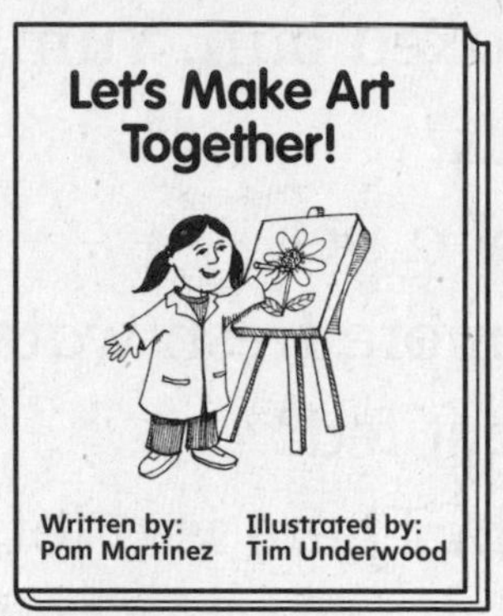

A. Look at the cover. Then answer the questions.

1. What is the title of this book?

____

2. Why is Tim Underwood's name on the cover of the book?

____

B. Write two sentences about something that you have made. Check your spacing as you write.

____

TEKS 1.1 (F) Identify the information that different parts of a book provide.
1.21 (A) Form upper- and lower-case letters legibly in text, using the basic conventions of print, including spacing between words and sentences.

Name ____________________

Practice

Phonics:
Long *o*: *o_e*,
Long *u*: *u_e*,
Long *e*: *e_e*

The letters **o_e** stand for the middle sound in **rope**.

The letters **u_e** stand for the middle sound in **cube**.

The letters **e_e** stand for the middle sound in **these**.

Read the word. Circle the picture that it names.

1. note

2. flute

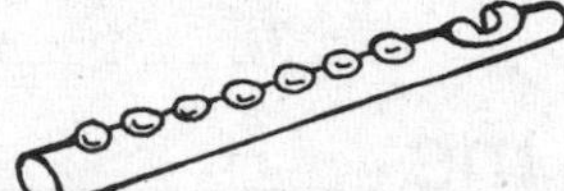

3. eve

4. Write a sentence using some of the words.

____

____

____

Name ______________________________

A. Write the word that completes each sentence.

find	after	old	new

1. Dad has ______________ socks for Kim because hers are ______________.

2. Can you help me ______________ my glasses?

3. We go to the park ______________ school.

B. Match the word to its meaning.

4. done — to do a job

5. work — finished

TEKS **1.3 (H)** Identify and read at least 100 high-frequency words from a commonly used list.

Name ______________________________

In some words, the letter ***k, g,*** or ***w*** is silent. Some consonant digraphs contain a silent letter.

Meg **kn**its. A **gn**at is not big. I **wr**ap the gift.

Write the word from the box that fits each clue. In words with *kn*, *gn*, or *wr*, the letters *k*, *g*, and *w*, are silent.

gnat	knee	knapsack
write	knife	wrist

1. This is a kind of bug. ______________
2. This body part is near your hand. ______________
3. This is also called a backpack. ______________
4. You do this with a pencil. ______________
5. This is in the middle of your leg. ______________
6. You use this to cut food. ______________

TEKS **1.3 (A) (iv)** Decode words in context and in isolation by applying common letter-sound correspondences, including consonant digraphs.

Name ______________________________

As you read Rose Robot Cleans Up, fill in the Conclusion Charts.

Inference	Inference

Conclusion

Inference	Inference

Conclusion

How do the Conclusion Charts help you better understand Rose Robot Cleans Up?

TEKS 1.9 (B) Describe characters in a story and the reasons for their actions and feelings.

Name ________________________________

You can use what you read and what you already know to help you **draw conclusions**.

Read each story. Draw a conclusion about the characters' actions and feelings. Fill in the circle of the sentence that makes the most sense.

1. Jane bikes to school. She likes to run races. She has fun jumping rope. Jane plays ball with her pals, too.

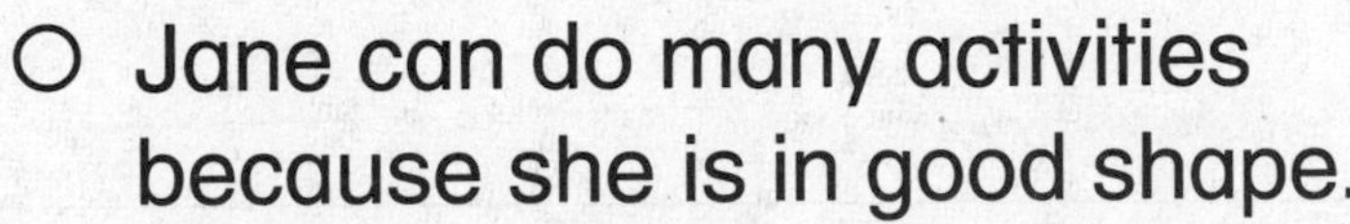

○ Jane can do many activities because she is in good shape.

○ Jane can do many activities because she likes to take care of dogs.

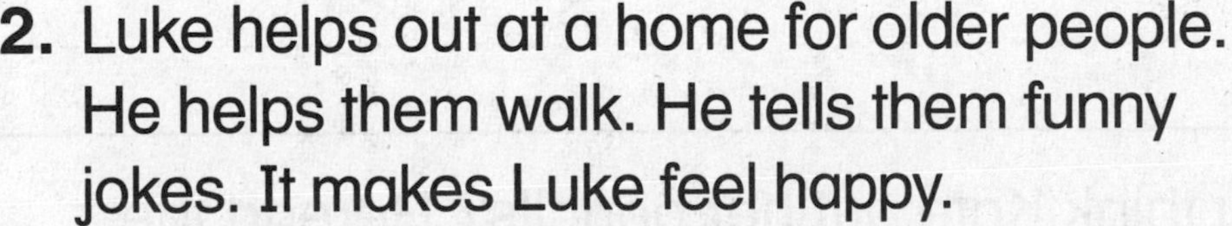

2. Luke helps out at a home for older people. He helps them walk. He tells them funny jokes. It makes Luke feel happy.

○ Luke feels happy because he is like the older people.

○ Luke feels happy because he likes to help older people.

Name ______________________________

Practice

Comprehension: Monitor Comprehension/ Reread

Good readers think about the story as they read. If they do not understand something in the story, they go back and read it again. This is called rereading.

Read the story. Then complete the items.

My name is Kate.
At school, we had to make old things into new things.
I used a box to make a pencil case.
When I was done, I put my pencils away.

1. Write a question that you would like to ask Kate about her pencil case.

____

2. Have you ever made something out of a box? What?

____

3. Where do you think Kate put her pencils? Reread the story to look for clues.

____

TEKS **1.4 (C)** Monitor comprehension, making corrections and adjustments when that understanding breaks down. **RC-1 (C)** Monitor and adjust comprehension. **RC-1 (F)** Make connections to own experiences.

Name ______________________________

Fiction tells about something that is made-up. Sometimes the characters are animals that act like people.

Read the story. Then answer the questions.

I go to school with my pals.
The bell rings. We swim in.
Our teacher tells us to stay away from hooks and sharks.
We eat kelp for lunch. Then we swim.
On my way home, I see a big worm.
Then I see the hook and line. I swim past fast.

1. Who is the main character in the story? Circle the best picture.

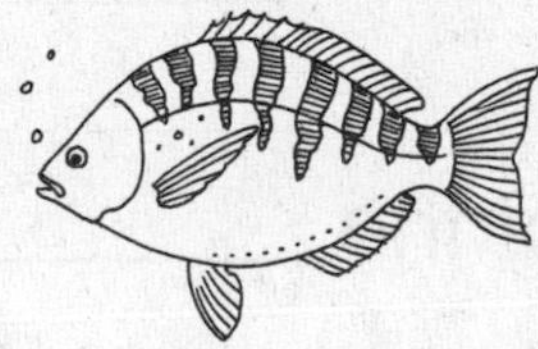

2. Why does a fish go fast when it sees a worm on a hook?

____

____

3. Think about what happened in this story. Tell a partner the story. Be sure to tell what happened in the beginning, the middle, and the end.

TEKS **1.9 (A)** Describe the plot (problem and solution) and retell a story's beginning, middle, and end with attention to the sequence of events. **1.9 (B)** Describe characters in a story and the reasons for their actions and feelings.

Name ______________________

Practice

Text Feature: Floor Plan

A **floor plan** is a drawing that shows where things are in a room.

Use the floor plan to complete each sentence.

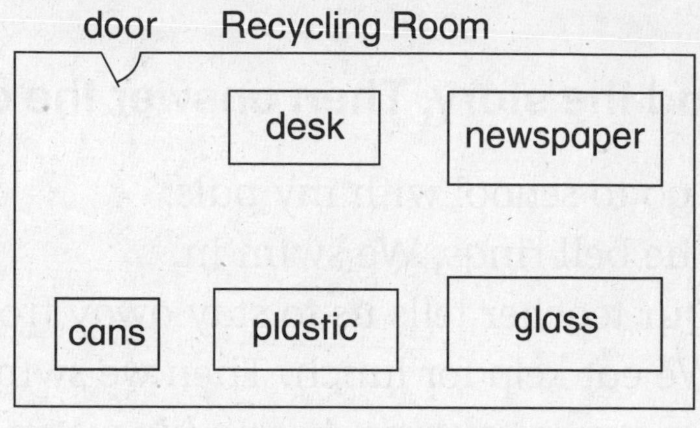

1. The cans bin is next to the ______________ bin.
2. If you can't tell which bin something goes in,

____

ask for help at the ______________.

3. Put  in the ______________ bin.

4. These  go in the ______________ bin.

5. The smallest bin is for ______________.

TEKS 1.14 (D) Use text features to locate specific information in text.
1.15 (B) Explain the meaning of specific signs and symbols.

Name ______________________________

Practice

Fluency: Choral Read: Expression

As I read, I will pay attention to the exclamation marks.

"Can you give me a ride to an apple grove?" asked Mole.
12 "I can not," yelled Fox.
17 So Mole rode his bike.
22 "These nice apples are big and red," said Mole.
31 He chose ten, used a net and a pole, and then rode home.
44 At home, Mole lit his stove.
50 "I will make a pie," he said. "I will read and cut and mix.
64 Then I will bake."
68 "I hope it tastes good," Mole said with a smile.
78 "I will put on a robe.
84 Then I will take a nap."
90 Soon, Mole's nose woke him up. Mole ate every bit.
100 "What can I say?" Mole smiled. "It's just the best!" 110

Comprehension Check

1. Why does Mole need a net and a pole?
2. What kind of pie does Mole make?

	Words Read	–	Number of Errors	=	Words Correct Score
First Read		–		=	
Second Read		–		=	

TEKS 1.5 Read aloud grade-level appropriate text with fluency and comprehension.
1.9 (B) Describe characters in a story and the reasons for their actions and feelings.

Name ______________________________

A. Look at the story. Draw a box around the first word you should read. Point to each word as you read the story.

Some days I walk to school. Some days I run.

Some days I ride to school. That is fun.

Every day at school is the best day.

I learn and play. I help the teacher in every way.

B. Find these uppercase and lowercase letters in the story and circle them:

d	w	r	S	E	h	t	I

C. Find these words in the story. Draw a line under them.

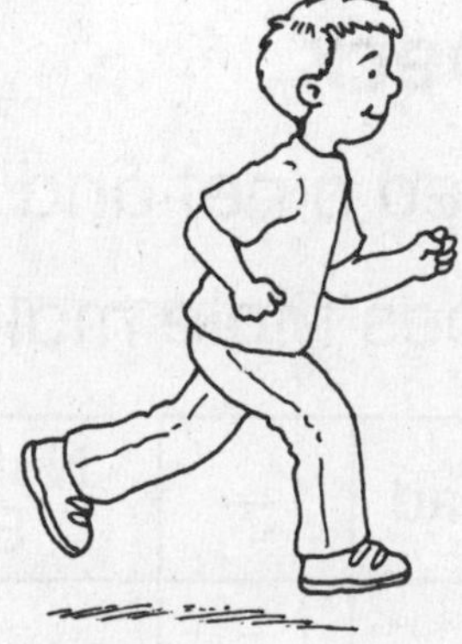

TEKS 1.1 (A) Recognize that spoken words are represented in written English by specific sequences of letters.
1.1 (B) Identify upper- and lower-case letters.

Name ______________________

Three letters can form a **blend**.
Listen for all three consonant sounds in each blend.

spring  **scr**atch  **spl**ash 

Listen for the digraph and the consonant sounds in this blend.

throw 

Write the new word on the line.
Connect the word to the matching picture.

1. scr + atch = ______________

2. str + ipe = ______________

3. spr + ing = ______________

4. spl + it = ______________

5. thr + ee = ______________

TEKS 1.3 (A) (iii) Decode words in isolation by applying common letter-sound correspondences, including consonant blends.

Name ______________________________

Practice

Oral Vocabulary: Nonfiction

Nonfiction tells about real people and events. It gives facts and details about real things.

Think about Schools Around the World. Then answer each question.

1. How do children in China learn math?

____

____

2. Tell about this article. Write 1 next to what you learned first. Write 2 next to what you learned later. Write 3 next to what you learned last.

______ Kids in Cuba like to swing around a pole at recess.

______ Kids who live in the desert in Egypt ride donkeys to school.

______ Kids in the mountains of Ecuador wear hats to school.

3. Circle the words in this list that tell about schools.

picture	ride	books
teachers	recess	small

TEKS **1.6 (D)** Identify and sort words into conceptual categories.
1.14 (B) Identify important facts or details in text, heard or read.
1.14 (C) Retell the order of events in a text by referring to the words.

Name ______________________________

Match each sentence to the picture that it explains.

1. The **girl** can do lots of tricks. **a.** 

2. The dog jumps into the **water**. **b.** 

3. Will my **friend** drop the books? **c.** 

4. **Does** the **boy** have fun with that rope? **d.** 

5. The kids have fun **by** the lake. **e.**  

6. Can you have **any** fun with a pet? **f.**  

TEKS **1.3 (H)** Identify and read at least 100 high-frequency words from a commonly used list.

Name ______________________________

When you add **-ed** or **-ing** to a word that ends with a vowel and a consonant, double the final consonant.

run + ing = ru**nn**ing — My dog is **running** fast.

chop + ed = cho**pp**ed — Sam **chopped** the log.

Read the sentence. Write the correct form of the word in the sentence.

1. Mike is ______________ the ball with a bat.
hit

2. The girl ______________ the nice red mug.
chip

3. The kids are ______________ the parts of the kite together.
put

4. My dog just ______________ over his dish.
tip

TEKS 1.3 (E) Read base words with inflectional endings.
1.22 (D) Spell base words with inflectional endings.

Name ______________________________

As you read Kids Have Fun!, fill in the Compare and Contrast Chart. Use words from the story.

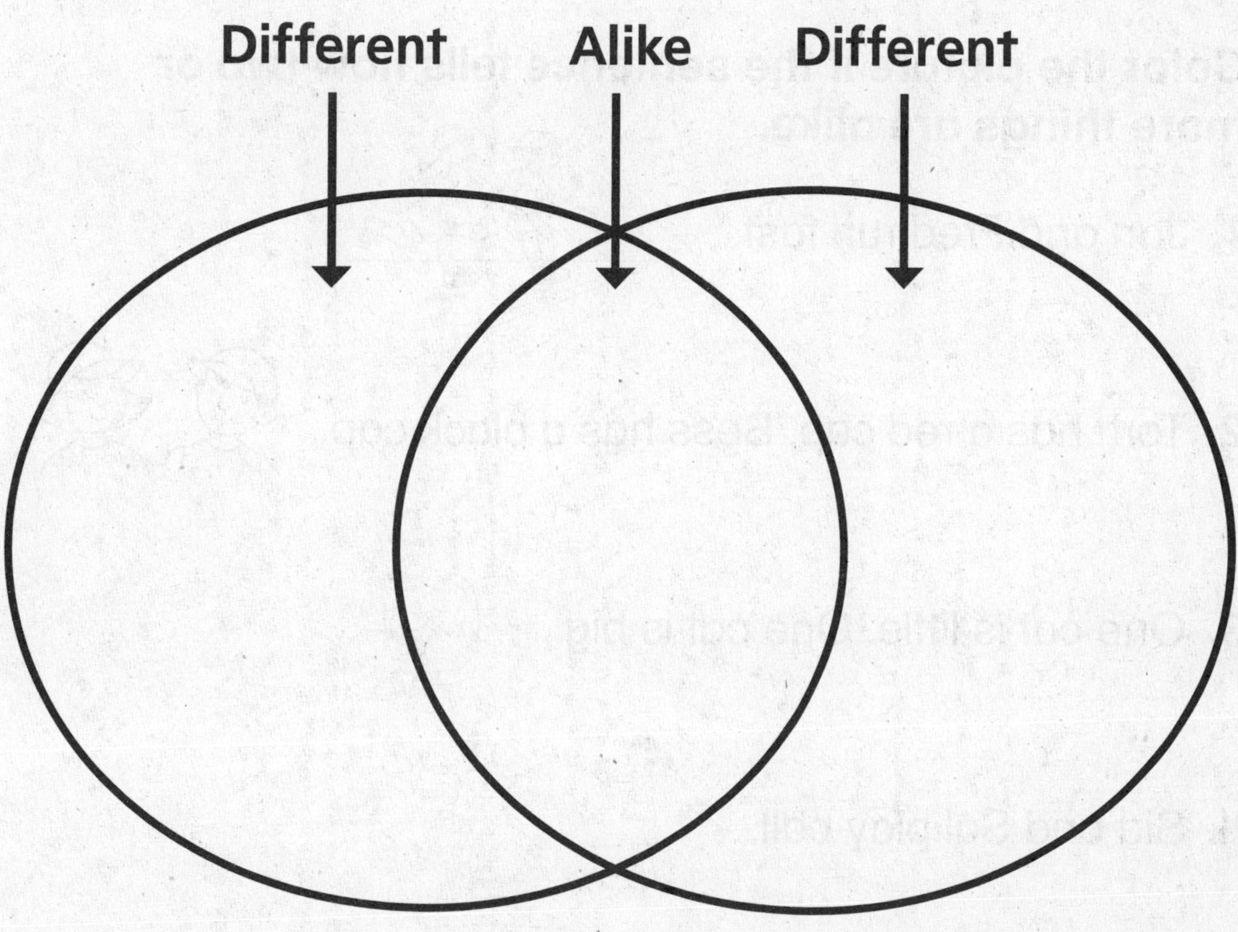

How does the Compare and Contrast Chart help you better understand the facts and details in Kids Have Fun!?

TEKS 1.14 (B) Identify important facts or details in text, heard or read.

Name ____________________

When you **compare** two or more things, you tell how they are **alike**.

When you **contrast** two or more things, you tell how they are **different**.

Color the picture if the sentence tells how two or more things are alike.

1. Jan and Fred run fast.

2. Tom has a red cap. Bess has a black cap.

3. One cat is little. One cat is big.

4. Sid and Sal play ball.

5. All the kids go to school.

6. Both girls like to play.

TEKS 1.9 (B) Describe characters in a story.

Name ______________________________

Practice

Comprehension: Monitor Comprehension/ Reread

Good readers think about the story as they read. If they do not understand something in the story, they go back and read it again. This is called rereading.

Read the story. Then answer the questions.

We have pen pals at school. Our teacher, Ms. White, helps us write to our pen pals. She sends the letters for us. Today, we got letters from our pen pals! They wrote that our letters made them feel happy. They said that they liked learning about other boys and girls. They hoped we could keep writing to them. That made us feel happy, too.

1. Do you think Ms. White's class will write more letters? Why? Reread the story to look for clues.

____

____

2. Whom do you think Ms. White's class is writing to? Why? Reread the story to look for clues.

____

____

3. To whom would you like to write a letter? Why?

____

____

TEKS **1.4 (C)** Monitor comprehension, making corrections and adjustments when that understanding breaks down. **RC-1 (C)** Monitor and adjust comprehension. **RC-1 (F)** Make connections to own experiences.

Name ______________________________

Writers use interesting and colorful words.

The **fluffy white** clouds float in the sky.

Circle the two words that a writer could use to describe each picture.

1. fast soft red

2. many little wet

3. black one hot

4. three big hot

5. little many big

6. hot stink yummy

TEKS 1.11 Recognize sensory details in literary text.

Name ______________________________

As I read, I will pay attention to punctuation.

I am Jon. I am six years old.
8 I am looking at photos.
13 I think it is so much fun.
20 Here I am with Mom and Dad.
27 Last spring, we went on a plane
34 to see Pop Streck.
38 I got a new knapsack!
42 This is Kim. Kim is five.
49 Kim has on a knit top. It has stripes and dots!
60 This big, black dog is Shag.
66 Shag made a splash in the mud.
73 After that, I had to scrub him and wring him out!
84 There is much more to see. But it is time for bed.
96 How can I save this spot? This string can save it! 107

Comprehension Check

1. What is Jon doing?

2. How are Jon and Kim different?

	Words Read	–	Number of Errors	=	Words Correct Score
First Read		–		=	
Second Read		–		=	

TEKS 1.3 (I) Monitor accuracy of decoding.
1.5 Read aloud grade-level appropriate text with fluency and compehension.

Name ______________________

The cover tells the **title**, or name, of the book. It tells the name of the **author**, or person who wrote the book. The cover also tells the **illustrator**, or person who made the pictures.

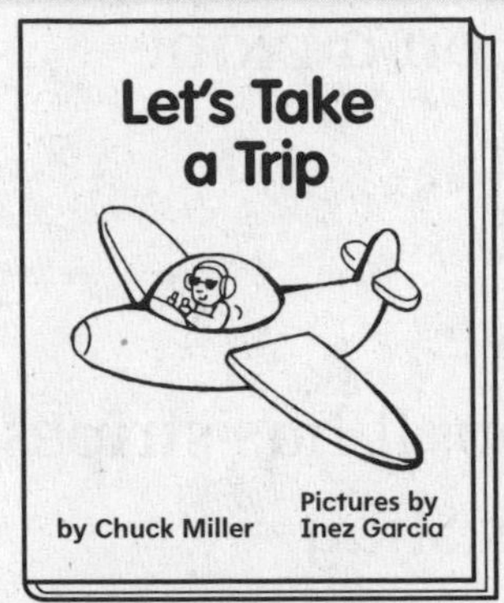

A. Look at the book cover. Then answer the questions.

1. What is the title of this book?

2. Who is the author of this book?

B. Write two sentences about a place that you would like to go. Check your spacing as you write.

TEKS **1.1 (F)** Identify the information that different parts of a book provide.
1.21 (A) Form upper- and lower-case letters legibly in text, using the basic conventions of print, including spacing between words and sentences.

Name ______________________________

The letters **ay** and **ai** stand for the **long /a/** sound.

Use a word from the box to complete each sentence.

snail	pay	paint	clay

1. Ray will use some ______________.

2. He will ______________ the vase gray.

3. She will ______________ for the tray.

4. A ______________ is on the pail.

TEKS 1.3 (A) (v) Decode words in context and in isolation by applying common letter-sound correspondences, including vowel digraphs.
1.3 (D) Decode words with common spelling patterns.

Name ______________________

Write a word from the box to complete each sentence.

once	upon	carry	eight	across	saw	walked

1. ______________ there were two chipmunks.

2. They ______________ some nuts to eat.

3. The nuts were ______________ the river.

4. The chipmunks wanted to ______________ the nuts back.

5. They ______________ on a log.

6. They put the nuts ______________ their heads.

7. They made ______________ trips.

TEKS **1.3 (H)** Identify and read at least 100 high-frequency words from a commonly used list.

Name ______________________________

As you read Drakes Tail, fill in the Predictions Chart.

What I Predict	What Happens

How does the Predictions Chart help you understand what happens in Drakes Tail?

TEKS **1.4 (A)** Confirm predictions about what will happen next in text by "reading the part that tells." **1.4 (C)** Monitor comprehension making corrections and adjustments when that understanding breaks down.

Name ______________________________

A **prediction** is a guess about what will happen next.
There is pizza on a plate. A good **prediction** would be that someone will eat the pizza.

Draw a line connecting each sentence with the one that tells what will happen next.

1. The block falls down.	Tim will pick it up.
2. The frog sees a pond.	The vet will help.
3. A dog is sick.	It will hop in.
4. Dad gets a cake.	She will run fast.
5. Jan gets a doll.	She will play with it.
6. Peg is late for school.	He will eat it.

Make your own prediction.

7. Jake has a gift from his friend Meg.

____

____

TEKS 1.4 (A) Confirm predictions about what will happen next in text by "reading the part that tells."

Name ______________________________

Good readers ask questions about the story as they read. If something is not clear go back and reread to answer your questions.

Read the story. Then answer the questions.

Today is field day at school. We pick teams. Tom is the smallest boy. Will anyone pick him? He is the last one picked. First, we have a relay race. Tom is not the fastest, but he tries to help the team. Then, we have to race to carry one of our teammates across the field. Tom is the lightest. Our team wins! Hooray for Tom!

1. How do you think Tom feels when he is the last one picked?
____
____
____

2. Write a question you have about the story.
____
____
____

3. Reread the story to look for clues to answer your question. Write an answer to your question.
____
____
____

TEKS 1.4 (B) Ask relevant questions, seek clarification, and locate facts and details about stories and other texts. RC-1 (B) Ask literal questions of text. RC-1 (D) Make inferences about text.

Name ____

Practice

Structural Analysis: Inflectional Endings: *-er*, *-est*

You can add **-er** or **-est** to compare two or more persons or things. The ending **-er** can mean "more." The ending **-est** can mean "most." Listen for the two sounds in **older** and **oldest** and in some of the other words ending in **-er** and **-est**.

A. Circle the word in each group that names something that is more than another thing.

1. fast	faster	fastest
2. newer	new	newest
3. dark	darkest	darker

B. Circle the word in each group that names something that is the most.

4. cold	coldest	colder
5. soon	sooner	soonest
6. small	smaller	smallest

TEKS **1.3 (E)** Read base words with inflectional endings.

Name ________________________________

A **dictionary** is a book that gives the meaning of words. Some words have more than one meaning.

Read the definitions below.

bark 1. the outside cover of a tree: The **bark** on the tree fell off. **2.** to make the sound that a dog makes: His dog will **bark** at all cats.

seal 1. an animal that lives in the ocean most of the time and swims very well: The **seal** swam over the wave. **2.** to close something so that it can not be opened: I had to **seal** the box with tape to close it.

Choose the correct definition for the word. Fill in the circle.

1. bark ○ drop a pole ○ sound like a dog

2. bark ○ part of a tree ○ in a pot

3. seal ○ run away ○ close a box very well

4. seal ○ a blue ship ○ an animal that swims

Use a word from above in a sentence.

____

TEKS **1.6 (E)** Use a dictionary to find words.

Name ______________________________

Practice

Fluency: Echo Read: Expression

As I read, I will pay attention to my expression.

Rain is on Mom's gray rug. Rain is in Mom's braid.
11 Rain is on Big Jay's tail.
17 There is so much water!
22 I get any pails I can find. I help Mom.
32 I catch a lot of rain.
38 The rain has stopped. May I run and play?
47 This yard has too much mud! Big Jay can't
use his house.
59 Big Jay sits and waits.
64 I see a big rainbow! It makes us smile.
73 It's a fine day after all! 79

Comprehension Check

1. What does the rain get on?

2. Why can't Big Jay use his house?

	Words Read	–	Number of Errors	=	Words Correct Score
First Read		–		=	
Second Read		–		=	

TEKS 1.3 (I) Monitor accuracy of decoding.
1.5 Read aloud grade-level appropriate text with fluency and comprehension.

Name ______________________________

A **song** has words called **lyrics** that are sung to music. The words have a **rhythm** and can **rhyme.** Many songs have a **chorus**, or lines that repeat. **Alliteration** is the same beginning sound in words.

Think about the song "Aiken Drum." Then answer the questions.

1. Work with a partner. Tell the words that repeat in "Aiken Drum." Take turns saying them aloud.
2. Say the first line of the song. Write the words that show alliteration. Circle the letters that stand for the beginning sound that is repeated.

____

3. Write a short poem about things you hear or see every day. Use words that rhyme, words that repeat, or words with the same beginning sounds if you wish. Make up a tune for your poem. Sing your song to a partner.

____

____

TEKS 1.8 Respond to and use rhythm, rhyme, and alliteration in poetry.
1.18 (B) Write short poems that convey sensory details.

Name ______________________________

Practice

Text Feature: Captions

Captions tell readers more about a photograph or picture.

Circle the caption that tells about the picture.

1. a snake
   a baby deer

2. Big Bass Lake
   the waterslide

3. my new bike
   Big Buck Forest

4. the swimming pool
   the campfire

5. our campsite
   last day of school

6. Dad's big catch!
   Sam's new dog

TEKS 1.14 (D) Use text features to locate specific information in text.

Name ______________________________

A **Reading Log** tells about something that you read.

Read a fiction book or a nonfiction book every day this week. Then tell about what you read.

Title ______________________________

Author ______________________________

What I Read About ______________________________

____

Title ______________________________

Author ______________________________

What I Read About ______________________________

____

TEKS **1.12** Read independently for a sustained period of time.
1.19 (C) Write brief comments on literary or informational texts.

Name ______________________________

Listen to the sound the letters **ee**, **ea**, **-e**, and **ie** stand for.

teeth 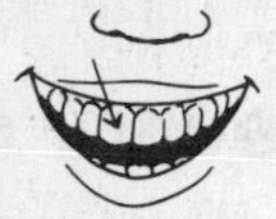 s**ea**l  h**e**  p**ie**ce 

Circle the word that names each picture. Then write the word.

1. sheet she ______________ 

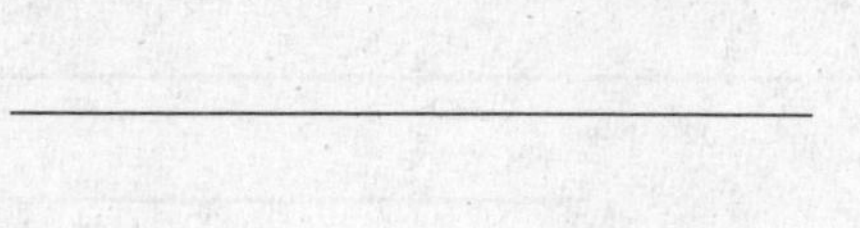

2. peel peek ______________ 

3. bean beak ______________ 

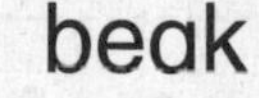

4. weak wheat ______________ 

5. piece peas ______________ 

6. eat eel ______________ 

TEKS **1.3 (A) (v)** Decode words in isolation by applying common letter-sound correspondences, including vowel digraphs.

Name ______________________

pretty says about give write were

Use the words from the box to complete the sentences.

1. Here is a book ____________ cats.

2. "What is it?" ____________ Gram.

3. "Did you ____________ it?" I ask.

4. I ____________ her the book.

5. The cover is ____________.

6. We ____________ glad we could read it.

TEKS 1.3 (H) Identify and read at least 100 high-frequency words from a commonly used list.

Name ______________________________

Practice

Comprehension: Character and Setting Chart

As you read Gram and Me, fill in the Character and Setting Chart.

Setting	What the Characters Do There
1.	1.
2.	2.
3.	3.
4.	4.

How does the Character and Setting Chart help you retell Gram and Me?

TEKS 1.4 (B) Locate facts and details about stories and other texts.
1.9 (B) Describe characters in a story.

Name ________________________________

The **setting** is where a story takes place.

The **characters** are the people or animals in a story.

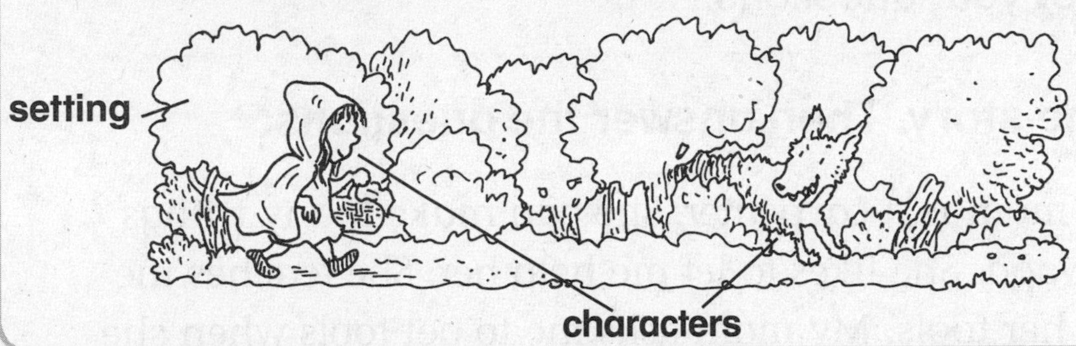

Think about stories that you have read about a school. Circle the people and things you would find in a school.

desk 

bike 

girl 

book 

pen 

skate 

animal 

boy 

TEKS 1.4 (B) Locate facts and details about stories and other texts.
1.9 (B) Describe characters in a story.

Name ______________________

Practice

Comprehension: Ask Questions

Good readers ask questions about the story as they read. If something is not clear go back and reread to answer your questions.

Read the story. Then answer the questions.

My mom is a carpenter. She can make many things with wood. She likes to let me help her. She teaches me about her tools. My mom asks me to get tools when she needs them. I love to help my mom!

1. How does the girl feel about her mom? How can you tell?

____

2. Write a question that you have about the story.

____

3. Now reread the story. Answer your question.

____

4. What is a carpenter? How do you know?

____

TEKS **1.4 (B)** Ask relevant questions, seek clarification, and locate facts and details about stories and other texts. **RC-1 (B)** Ask literal questions of text. **RC-1 (D)** Make inferences about text.

Name ______________________________

Practice

Phonics: Long *e* Words Ending with Silent *e*

Some words with long **e** have a silent **e** at the end. The word **please** has the long **e** sound and silent **e** at the end.

Circle the long *e* word in each group that ends with a silent *e*.

1. leave	cookie	me
2. see	sea	piece
3. eve	she	bee
4. we	these	three
5. be	tea	cheese
6. please	pea	glee
7. flea	tree	sleeve
8. geese	he	free

TEKS **1.3 (A) (v)** Decode words in isolation by applying common letter-sound correspondences, including vowel digraphs. **1.3 (C) (iv)** Use common syllabication patterns to decode words, including vowel-consonant-silent "e" words.

Name ______________________

Practice

Vocabulary Strategy: Compound Words

A **compound word** is made up of smaller words.

ant + hill = anthill

yard	fall	boat	house

A. Put a word from the box with each word below to make a compound word. Write the compound word on the line.

1. rain ______________
2. back ______________
3. dog ______________
4. sail ______________

B. Circle the compound word. Then draw a line between the two smaller words.

5. grandmother mother
6. bed bedtime
7. flowerpot flower
8. catnap nap
9. book storybook

TEKS 1.3 (F) Use knowledge of the meaning of base words to identify and read common compound words.

Name ______________________________

As I read, I will pay attention to my expression.

Once upon a time, Fox had a funny dream. He
10 dreamed of grapes. Then Fox woke up fast.
18 "It's late June," said Fox. "Days are hot and
27 sunny. The grapes will be ripe. I know I can
37 find them." Fox set off across the hill. "Green
46 grapes are for me," said Fox. "I'll eat all that I
57 see." Fox had a nose for grapes. He saw lots
67 of them. They sat way up on vines on tree
77 branches in a field. Fox went after the grapes.
86 He ran faster to gain speed. Then he jumped
95 way up. But he couldn't reach them. Fox rose
104 up on his feet. But it was no use. He just
115 couldn't reach. At last Fox gave up. "This is
124 silly," Fox said. "I don't want those grapes.
132 They are not that great." 137

Comprehension Check

1. What did Fox dream about?

2. Why did Fox decide that he did not want the grapes?

	Words Read	–	Number of Errors	=	Words Correct Score
First Read		–		=	
Second Read		–		=	

TEKS **1.3 (I)** Monitor accuracy of decoding.
1.5 Read aloud grade-level appropriate text with fluency and comprehension.

Name ______________________________

Practice

Read Aloud: Realistic Fiction

Realistic fiction stories tell about made-up events that seem like they could really happen.

Listen to the story. Then answer the questions.

As I ride on the bus to school, my eyes are closing. I was up too late last night playing on the computer. Suddenly, my eyes open and I am awake. "Oh, no! I left my homework on the table!" I think about how sad my teacher will be. I think this might not be a good day.

1. Write to tell how the character feels at the beginning of the story. Circle the clues in the story that help you know.

____

____

2. What is the character's problem? Circle the best answer.
His computer is broken.
His homework is at home.

3. Write about a time when you forgot something.

____

____

____

TEKS **1.7 (A)** Connect the meaning of a well-known story to personal experiences. **1.9 (A)** Describe the plot (problem and solution). **1.9 (B)** Describe characters in a story and the reasons for their actions and feelings.

Name ______________________________

A **numerical list** is a series of things written in **1, 2, 3** order.

Make two lists. Use the words below to help you.

pen	pants	tape
hat	desk	socks

Things for a Trip

1. ______________________________
2. ______________________________
3. ______________________________

Things for School

1. ______________________________
2. ______________________________
3. ______________________________

Draw a picture of something else you need at school.

TEKS 1.6 (D) Identify and sort words into conceptual categories.

Name ______________________

Practice

Reading Log

A **Reading Log** tells about something that you read.

Read a fiction book or a nonfiction book every day this week. Then tell about what you read.

Title ______________________

Author ______________________

What I Read About ______________________

____

Title ______________________

Author ______________________

What I Read About ______________________

____

____

TEKS **1.12** Read independently for a sustained period of time.
1.19 (C) Write brief comments on literary or informational texts.

Name ______________________

The long **o** vowel sound is spelled **o, oa, ow,** and **oe.**

cold **coat** **snow** **doe**

coat	toe	hold	snow	fold	toad

Write a word from the box to name each picture.

1. 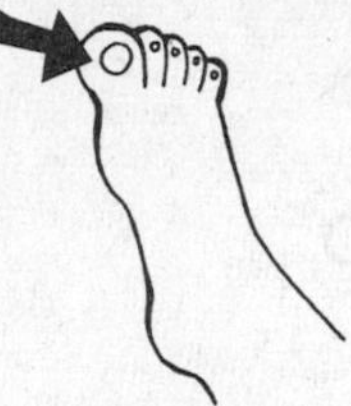
____

2. 
____

3. 
____

4. 
____

5. 
____

6. 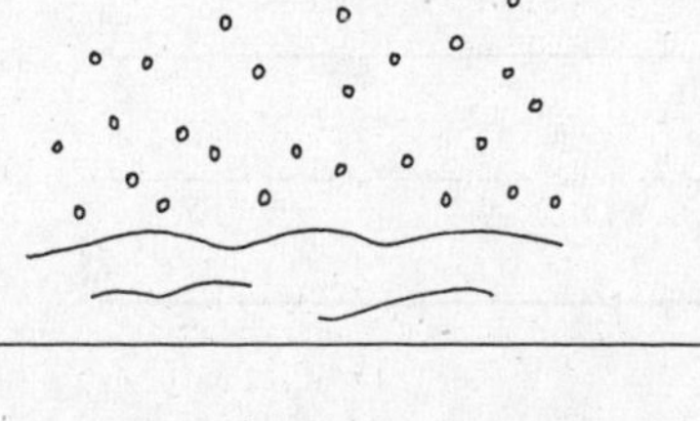
____

TEKS 1.3 (A) (v) Decode words in isolation by applying common letter-sound correspondences, including vowel digraphs.

Name ______________________________

better	buy	change	difficult	move	ripe

Use a word from the box to complete each sentence.

Did you just ____________ here? We have

a ____________ problem. We want to

____________ an ugly lot into a pretty lot. I have

an idea. We can use our money to ____________

seeds. We can plant peppers and pick them when they are

____________. Flowers can make the garden even

____________!

TEKS 1.3 (H) Identify and read at least 100 high-frequency words from a commonly used list.

Name ______________________________

As you read César Chávez, fill in the Retelling Chart.

Retell
____
____
____
____

How does the Retelling Chart help you understand César Chávez?

TEKS 1.14 (C) Retell the order of events in a text by referring to the words.

Name ________________________

Practice

Comprehension: Retell

When you **retell** a selection, tell the events in order. Use your own words.

Look at the pictures. Write what happens in each picture.

1. 

First, ________________________

Next, ________________________

Last, ________________________

2. 

First, ________________________

Next, ________________________

Last, ________________________

TEKS **1.14 (C)** Retell the order of events in a text by referring to the words.

Name ____________________________

Good readers **ask questions** as they read. If something is not clear, reread to answer your questions.

Read the story. Then answer the questions.

My grandma says that we must work to make the world a better place. My grandma does this every day. She knits blankets for babies at the hospital. I help her drop them off. She takes her friends to the store when they can't go alone. I help them carry the food. My grandma shows me how I can make the world better, even when I am still little.

1. Write a question you have about the story.

____

____

2. Now reread the story. Write the answer to your question.

____

____

3. How does the child feel about her grandma? How do you know?

____

____

TEKS **1.4 (B)** Ask relevant questions, seek clarification, and locate facts and details about stories and other texts. **RC-1 (B)** Ask literal questions of text. **RC-1 (D)** Make inferences about text.

Name ______________________________

Practice

Phonics: Two-Syllable Words

Some words have two parts, or **syllables**. You can break a word into syllables to help you read it.

A. Put the two syllables together. Write the word on the line. Then match the word to the picture it names.

1. car rot 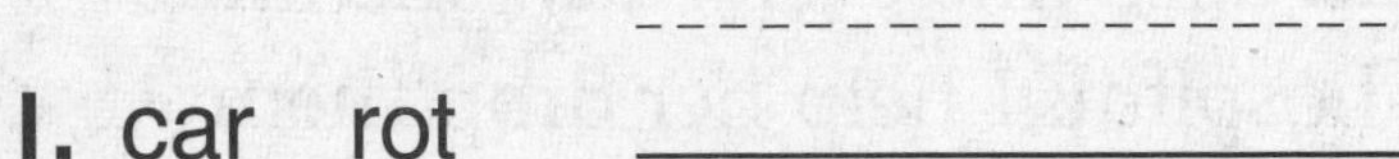 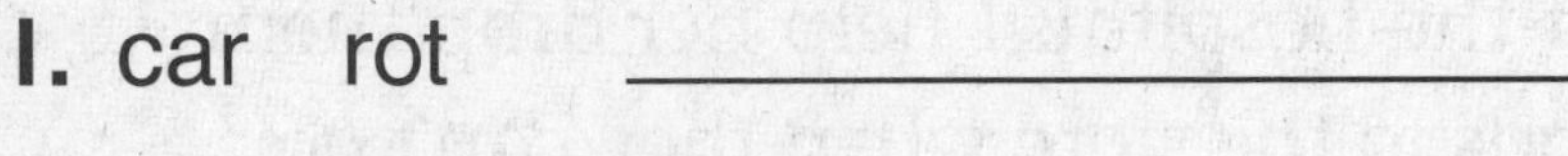

2. pi lot 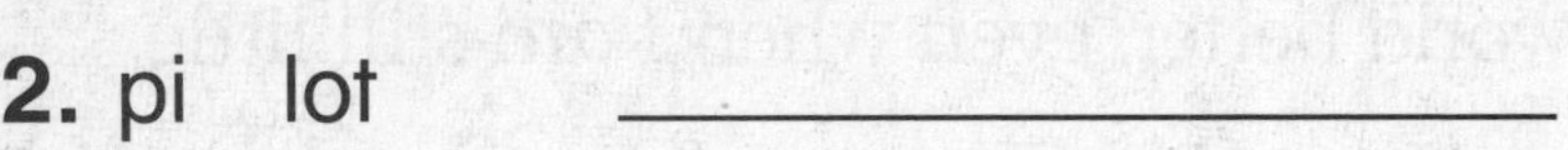

3. bas ket 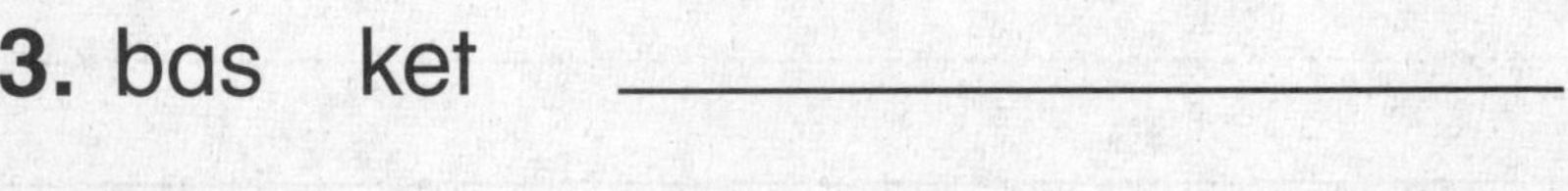

4. kick ing 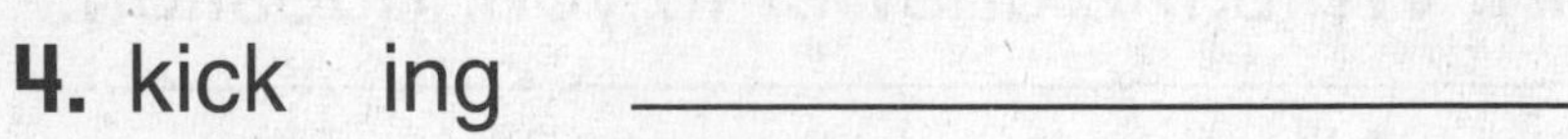

B. Divide each word into syllables. Then write each syllable.

rabbit

_______ • _______

began

_______ • _______

TEKS 1.2 (D) Blend spoken phonemes to form two-syllable words.

Name ____________________

Context clues are words that help you figure out the meaning of a new word. Context clues may be found in the same sentence or in nearby sentences.

Use the <u>underlined</u> context clues to figure out the meaning of the word in bold letters. Then match the word to its meaning. Write the correct letter on the line. Use a dictionary to check your work.

a. give what someone wants or can use
b. dirt
c. gather plants that are ready
d. plants used for food
e. plan for a group to do

1. Our town <u>planned</u> a **project** we could <u>work</u> on <u>together</u>. ____

2. The **crops** from our <u>gardens</u> will <u>feed</u> people who are <u>hungry</u>. ____

3. These bushes **provide** the berries <u>we</u> <u>need</u> to make pies. ____

4. When they are <u>full</u> and <u>ripe</u>, we will **harvest** them. ____

5. The **soil** in this field is very good for <u>growing plants</u>. ____

TEKS **1.6 (C)** Determine what words mean from how they are used in a sentence, either heard or read. **1.6 (E)** Use a dictionary to find words.

Name ______________________________________

As I read, I will pay attention to the phrasing.

"This old lot is a mess," says Flo.
08 "I wish it were pretty."
13 Jo and Mo load trash. Flo holds the
21 bag. Flo's dad mows. The goat mows, too!
29 Flo says, "Now let's grow."
34 Flo, Jo, and Mo plant seeds all about.
42 "Please don't grow slow!" says Flo. "Go, go, go!"
51 "Give it time," says Dad.
56 See what has grown. It is so pretty! Each
65 row glows! 67

Comprehension Check

1. What do Jo and Mo do first?

2. What happens at the end of the story?

	Words Read	–	Number of Errors	=	Words Correct Score
First Read		–		=	
Second Read		–		=	

TEKS **1.3 (I)** Monitor accuracy of decoding.
1.5 Read aloud grade-level appropriate text with fluency and comprehension.

Name ____________________________________

A **telephone directory** lists names, addresses, and telephone numbers.

Vann,	Jay	17 Elm Ave.	555-5436
Vann,	Max	17 Elm Ave.	555-5436
Wade,	Jake	245 Main St.	555-7401
Wade,	Lon	29 Sunset Ave.	555-4269
Wade,	May	9 Sunrise St.	555-9711

Use the directory to complete each question.

1. How many people have the last name Wade? ______

2. What is May Wade's phone number? ______________

3. Where does Jake Wade live? ______________

4. Who has the same address and telephone number?

____

____

TEKS 1.14 (D) Use text features to locate specific information in text.
1.24 (B) Use text features in age-appropriate reference works to locate information.

Name ________________________________

A **fable** is a short story that teaches a lesson. The characters in a fable are usually animals that talk.

Listen to the fable. Then answer the questions.

One day, a lion caught a mouse. The lion wanted to eat the mouse for lunch. The mouse squeaked, "Please, big lion. Do not eat me. One day, I may be able to help you!" The lion said, "You help me? That is so funny, I will let you go." "Thank you," said the mouse.

The next day, the lion was trapped in a net. He could not move. He roared. The mouse came running to help. He bit at the net until the lion was free. "Thank you, mouse," said the lion. The mouse said, "Now you can see that one small mouse can help a big lion."

1. What is the lesson of the story? Circle the best answer.

   Be kind to people, and they will be kind to you.
   Slow and steady wins the race.
   Working together makes you better.

2. Tell about one nice thing that you have done for someone else.

   ____

   ____

TEKS 1.7 (A) Connect the meaning of a well-known fable to personal experiences.

Name ____________________

A **Reading Log** tells about something that you read.

Read a fiction book or a nonfiction book every day this week. Then tell about what you read.

Title ____________________

Author ____________________

What I Read About ____________________

Title ____________________

Author ____________________

What I Read About ____________________

TEKS **1.12** Read independently for a sustained period of time.
1.19 (C) Write brief comments on literary or informational texts.

Name ______________________________

Say the words. Then listen to the **long /i/** sound.

chi**l**d   fl**y**   h**igh**   p**ie**

Write the word that completes the sentence.

1. Meg's kite will ______________ over the trees.

try   fly   cry

2. Pam will ______________ her shoe.

try   tie   pie

3. We eat lunch together on a ______________ hill.

might   high   fly

4. Let's wave to that plane in the ______________.

my   sky   cry

5. The ______________ can walk to his house.

mild   child   cut

TEKS 1.3 (A) (v) Decode words in context by applying common letter-sound correspondences, including vowel digraphs.

Name ______________________

Write the letter of the word from the box that completes each sentence.

a. head	**b.** never	**c.** should	**d.** ball
e. shout	**f.** meadow	**g.** Perhaps	

1. The boys and girls _____ for the team.

2. The big kite was flying high over Kim's _____.

3. Ben is _____ late for the school bus.

4. We _____ get a new bat and _____ at the shop.

5. _____ we can ride together in the green _____ today.

TEKS 1.3 (H) Identify and read at least 100 high-frequency words from a commonly used list.

Name ____________________

As you read The Kite, think about the plot. Then fill in the Plot Chart.

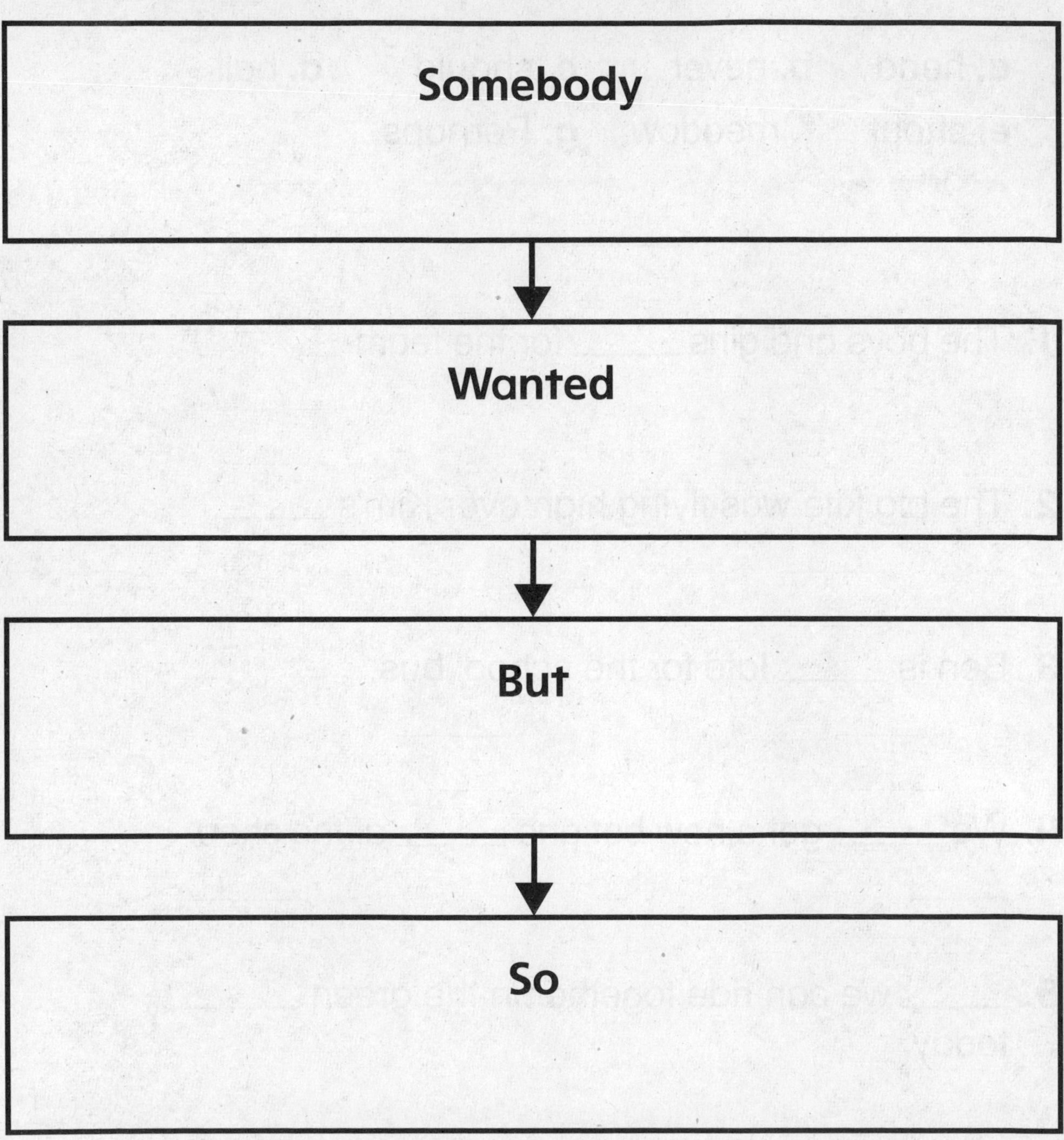

How does the Plot Chart help you better understand The Kite?

TEKS 1.9 (A) Describe the plot (problem and solution).

Practice

Comprehension: Plot

Name ___________________________

As you read the story about Will, think about the plot. Then answer the questions.

Will can't fly his new kite. He runs down the street with his kite. Still the kite can't fly high. Then Will takes his kite to Mike's house. The two friends try to pull the kite. But the kite just comes down again. Perhaps there is more wind on the high hill in the meadow. That is the best idea yet. Now Will's kite can fly in the wind.

1. What problem does Will have in the story?

____

2. What solution does Will try first?

____

3. What solution does Will try next?

____

4. How does the kite finally fly?

____

TEKS 1.9 (A) Describe the plot (problem and solution).

Name ______________________________

When you **visualize** you use the words you read to make pictures in your mind. Think about how the words help you understand how things sound, smell, look, and feel.

Read the story. Then answer the questions.

I catch the ball. I hear shouts and cheers. I smell the cold night air and the damp grass. I run with my head down. The ball is tucked under my arm. I try to run to the right. CRASH! I fly into the air. I try to sit up. I see lights and stars. My team tries to help me up. It is a good thing that I have my helmet and pads! I am okay. I still have the ball!

1. What game is the boy playing? Reread the story to look for clues and circle the best answer.

baseball   basketball   football

2. Write one thing from the story that the player

hears: ____________________   **sees:** ____________________

smells: ____________________   **feels:** ____________________

TEKS RC-1 (C) Monitor and adjust comprehension.

Name ______________________________

Practice

Structural Analysis: Inflectional Ending: *-ed*

For verbs that end with a consonant followed by **y** change the **y** to **i** before adding **-ed**.

fry fried

Read the verb under each sentence. Show that the action happened in the past. Change the *y* to *i* and add *-ed* to the verb. Then complete the sentence.

1. They ______________ puppies at the pet store.
spy

2. Jenny ______________ her wet hand.
dry

3. Nathan ______________ to catch the bus.
try

4. We ______________ to the letter.
reply

TEKS **1.3 (C) (i) (ii)** Use common syllabication patterns to decode words, including closed syllable (CVC) and open syllable (CV).
1.3 (E) Read base words with inflectional endings.

Name ________________________________

Practice

Vocabulary Strategy: Inflected Verbs and Word Parts

A verb is a word that shows action.
You can add **-ed** or **-ing** to most verbs.
A verb with an **-ed** ending means the action happened in the past.

play + **ing** = playing

play + **ed** = played

A. Write each verb with -ing and -ed.

1. flash ____________ ____________

2. pull ____________ ____________

3. fill ____________ ____________

B. Use an -ing word and -ed word in sentences.

4. ________________________________

____

TEKS 1.3 (E) Read base words with inflectional endings.
1.6 (A) Identify words that name actions.

Name ______________________________

Practice

Fluency: Choral Read: Expression

As I read, I will pay attention to the dialogue and how it affects expression.

The bright sun is high in the sky.
08 My coach yells, "Try to win! Try, try!"
16 It's a high fly! I try to find it. The bright sun
28 blinds me.
30 "Move to the right!" yells Dwight. "Then
37 you might see better."
41 Dwight is right. The light changes. I catch
49 the fly. It's a tie. Fans go wild!
57 "Thanks, Dwight," I sigh. "You are kind."
64 "We are a team," he says. 70

Comprehension Check

1. What does the sun do to the high fly?

2. Why does Dwight say "Move to the right!"?

	Words Read	–	Number of Errors	=	Words Correct Score
First Read		–		=	
Second Read		–		=	

TEKS 1.3 (I) Monitor accuracy of decoding.
1.5 Read aloud grade-level appropriate text with fluency and comprehension.

Name ______________________________

A **folktale** is a story that has been retold for many years. Folktales often have phrases that repeat.

Listen to the folktale. Then answer the questions.

Once upon a time, a kind old woman made a gingerbread man. After he was baked, he jumped up and ran away. He shouted, "Run, run, as fast as you can! You can't catch me! I'm the gingerbread man!" He ran past a cow. The cow tried to eat him, but he was too fast. He shouted, "Run, run, as fast as you can! You can't catch me! I'm the gingerbread man!" All at once, the gingerbread man came to a big river. What could he do? A fox came by. The fox said, "I can help you. I will give you a ride across the river. Just sit on my head!" The gingerbread man was not very smart. He jumped on the fox's head and away they swam. When they came to the middle of the river, the fox tossed the gingerbread man up, up, up in the air. And the gingerbread man did not live happily ever after.

1. Circle the phrase that you find at the beginning of most folktales and fairy tales.

   Once upon a time They lived happily ever after.

2. What does this phrase tell you? Circle the best answer.

   This is a true story. This is a made-up story.

TEKS 1.7 (B) Explain the function of recurring phrases in traditional folk tales.

Name ______________________

A **chart** gives information in an organized way.

Read the chart.

Things Frog Ate	Things Toad Ate
plums 1	peaches 2
apples 2	plums 3
grapes 8	eggs 3
eggs 2	grapes 10

Count the things Frog and Toad ate and complete the sentences.

1. Frog ate ______________ eggs.

2. Toad ate ______________ grapes.

3. Frog ate ______________ plum.

4. Toad ate ______________ peaches.

TEKS 1.14 (D) Use text features to locate specific information in a text.

Name ______________________

A **Reading Log** tells about something that you read.

Read a fiction book or a nonfiction book every day this week. Then tell about what you read.

Title ______________________

Author ______________________

What I Read About ______________________

Title ______________________

Author ______________________

What I Read About ______________________

TEKS 1.12 Read independently for a sustained period of time.
1.19 (C) Write brief comments on literary or informational texts.

Name ______________________________

Sometimes the letter **y** and the letters **ey** stand for the **long /e/** sound.

happ**y** monk**ey**

Circle the word that answers the question. Then write the word.

1. What can you spend? ______________

muddy penny

2. What can you use to lock a door? ______________

money key

3. What do you call a baby dog? ______________

daisy puppy

4. What can you call a rabbit? ______________

bunny easy

TEKS **1.3 (A) (ii)** Decode words in context and in isolation by applying common letter-sound correspondences, including single letters (vowels). **1.3 (C) (i) (ii)** Use common syllabication patterns to decode words, including closed syllable (CVC) and open syllable (CV).

Name ______________________

blue because until other also or

Write the word that completes each sentence.

1. The team flag is ____________ and white.

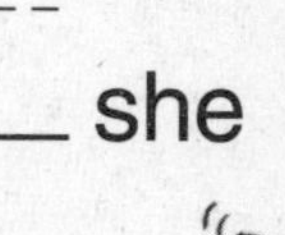

2. Jan is good at soccer ____________ she can run fast.

3. The ____________ girls run fast, ____________.

4. The team may ____________ may not win.

5. The girls play ____________ it is dark.

TEKS 1.3 (H) Identify and read at least 100 high-frequency words from a commonly used list.

Name ______________________________

As you read Animal Teams, fill in the Retelling Chart.

Retell
______________________________ ______________________________ ______________________________ ______________________________

How does the information you wrote in this Retelling Chart help you retell Animal Teams?

TEKS **1.14 (A)** Restate the main idea, heard or read.
1.14 (B) Identify important facts or details in text, heard or read.
1.14 (C) Retell the order of events in a text by referring to the words.

Name ______________________

Practice

Comprehension: Retell

When you **retell** a passage, you tell only the important parts.

Read the passage. Then look at it again. Underline the sentences that retell the passage.

What will we see in an ant nest?
The worker ants bring in things to eat.
Some take things to eat to the queen.
The queen does not get food.
She stays in the nest.
The queen ant lays eggs.

Draw three pictures to retell the story.

TEKS 1.14 (A) Restate the main idea, heard or read.
1.14 (B) Identify important facts or details in text, heard or read.
1.14 (C) Retell the order of events in a text by referring to words.

Practice

Name ______________________________

Comprehension: Visualize

When you **visualize** you use the words you read to make pictures in your mind. Think about how the words help you understand how things sound, smell, look, and feel.

Read the story. Then answer the questions.

Today Jane is going to the shelter to pick out a new dog! Jane wants a dog that likes to play. At the shelter, there is a big room. Jane looks at the dogs for a long time. There is one dog that looks at Jane. It is a small white dog with black spots. The dog walks to Jane. It sits on Jane's feet. The dog wags its tail. Jane pets the dog. Its fur is short and soft. Jane knows that this is the dog for her.

1. What kind of dog does Jane want? Reread the story to look for clues. Circle the clues.

2. What does Jane's new dog look like?

____

____

3. How do you think Jane feels at the end of the story? How do you know?

____

____

TEKS RC-1 (C) Monitor and adjust comprehension.
RC-1 (D) Make inferences about text.

Name ______________________

Practice

Structural Analysis: Inflectional Ending: *-ed*

If a verb ends in a **consonant + y**, change the **y** to **i** before adding **-ed**. Do this for verbs with one syllable or two syllables.

cry + ed = cr**i**ed   stu**dy** + ed = studi**ed**

Write the word that completes each sentence.

1. The baby ______________.

cried   cryed

2. Han ______________ his hands.

dryed   dried

3. Kelly ______________ the big bike.

tried   tryed

4. Dad ______________ the fish.

fryed   fried

TEKS 1.3 (E) Read base words with inflectional endings.

Name ______________________________

Context clues are words in a sentence that help you figure out the meaning of a new word.

Use the underlined context clues to figure out the meaning of the word in bold letters.

1. The apples are **falling** down to the ground.

2. The branches and leaves hide animals in the **forest**.

3. I **heard** the owl hoot.

4. The rabbit hopped into the bush **before** the fox saw it.

Now match the word to its meaning:

1. falling — a. listened with ears

2. forest — b. to go from a high place to a low place

3. heard — c. at an earlier time

4. before — d. a place where trees and plants grow

TEKS 1.6 (C) Determine what words mean from how they are used in a sentence, either heard or read.

Name ______________________________

Practice

Fluency: Choral Read: Expression

As I read, I will pay attention to the dialogue and how it affects expression.

"Piggy!" shout Bunny and Ducky. "Your home
07 is so messy and dirty!"
12 "You should never be so sloppy," says Billy. "We
21 will help you clean."
25 Bunny finds smelly jelly. Ducky finds rusty, dusty
33 cans. They toss them out. Billy wipes a muddy
42 bat. He cleans a sticky key. Piggy is happy.
51 The time flies by. "Golly!" shouts Piggy.
58 "Now my home isn't messy. I am lucky!
66 Thank you!" 68

Comprehension Check

1. Who helps Piggy clean?

2. Why is Piggy lucky?

	Words Read	–	Number of Errors	=	Words Correct Score
First Read		–		=	
Second Read		–		=	

TEKS **1.3 (I)** Monitor accuracy of decoding.
1.5 Read aloud grade-level appropriate text with fluency and comprehension.

Name ______________________________

A **fable** is a short story that teaches a lesson. The characters in a fable are usually animals that talk.

Listen to the fable. Then answer the questions.

Once upon a time, two frogs were friends. One frog lived in a nice, wet swamp. The other frog lived in a rut made by car wheels in the road. The rut had water only when it rained. The swamp frog tried and tried to get his friend to move to the swamp. He said, "It is safer in the swamp. There are no cars." But the road frog said, "I am used to my rut. I do not want to change." One day, a car came by while the road frog was sitting in his rut. The wheel of the car went into the rut, and the frog went flying into the air. As he landed in the swamp, he said, "You were right. It is not good to stay in a rut."

1. What is the lesson of this story? Circle the best answer.

   Be kind to others. Change can be good.

2. What is something new that you would like to try so that you don't get stuck in a rut?

   ____

   ____

TEKS 1.7 (A) Connect the meaning of a well-known fable to personal experiences.

Name ______________________________

A poem often **repeats** words or sentences more than once. This gives the poem **rhythm**.

Read the poem. Then answer the questions.

The Pelican and the Fish

The fish swims.
The pelican flies over.
The fish swims.
The pelican is hungry.
The fish swims.
The pelican dives down.
The fish swims.

____

The pelican ______________________________
GULP!

1. Circle the sentences that repeat.

2. Complete the end of the poem.

TEKS 1.8 Respond to and use rhythm in poetry.

Name ______________________

Practice

Reading Log

A **Reading Log** tells about something that you read.

Read a fiction book or a nonfiction book every day this week. Then tell about what you read.

Title ______________________

Author ______________________

What I Read About ______________________

Title ______________________

Author ______________________

What I Read About ______________________

TEKS 1.12 Read independently for a sustained period of time.
1.19 (C) Write brief comments on literary or informational texts.

Name ______________________

Practice

Phonics: *r*-Controlled Vowels *er*, *ir*, *ur*

The letters **er**, **ir**, and **ur** stand for the same sound.

cl**er**k b**ir**d t**ur**n

Circle the word that names the picture. Then write the word on the line.

1. girl
   gull ______________________

2. cot
   curl ______________________

3. fun
   fern ______________________

4. spurs
   spots ______________________

5. hid
   her ______________________

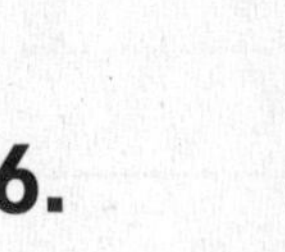
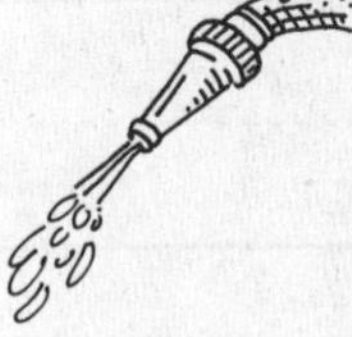

6. squirt
   squint ______________________

TEKS **1.3 (C) (vi)** Use common syllabication patterns to decode words, including r-controlled vowel sounds.

Name ____________________

full Poor another climbed through lucky leaped

A. Write the word that completes each sentence.

1. Skunk ____________ slowly out of her den.

2. She was hungry. ____________ Skunk!

3. Then she ____________ up and saw ____________ den.

4. How ____________ she was! The den was ____________ of things to eat!

5. A head poked ____________.

B. Write a sentence to complete the story.

6. ____________________

TEKS 1.3 (H) Identify and read at least 100 high-frequency words from a commonly used list.

Name ______________________________

Practice

Comprehension: Cause and Effect Chart

As you read Kitten's First Full Moon, fill in the Cause and Effect Chart.

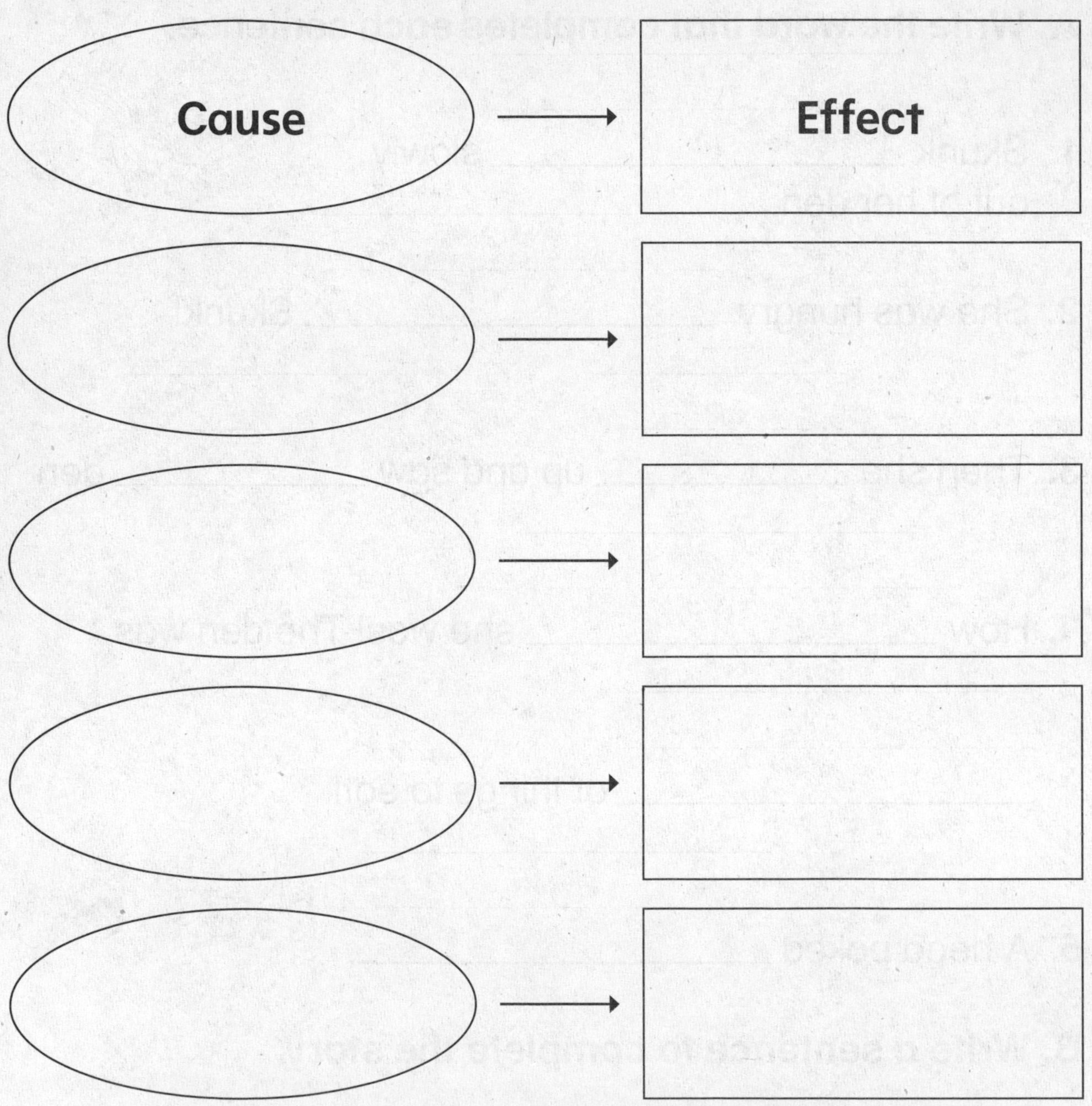

How does the information you wrote in this Cause and Effect Chart help you retell Kitten's First Full Moon?

TEKS 1.9 (B) Describe characters in a story and the reasons for their actions.

Name ____________________

The **cause** is why something happens.

The **effect** is what happens.

cause  effect 

Match the cause to the effect.

1. The dog had a bath.

2. The girl fell.

3. Bob stepped on the box.

4. The tire is flat.

5. Ben ran faster than the others.

6. It is raining.

TEKS **1.9 (B)** Describe characters in a story and the reasons for their actions.

Name ______________________

Practice

Comprehension: Ask Questions

Good readers **ask questions** about the story as they read. If they are not sure about something, they go back and reread the story to figure it out.

Read the story. Then answer the questions.

I like to look up at the sky. Today the sun is out. The sky is blue. I see white fluffy clouds. Oh, no! Now it is getting darker. The wind is getting stronger. I see a flash of lightning. I hear a rumble of thunder. I run inside. I like to watch the lightning. I count how long it takes until I hear thunder. This way I can tell if the storm is coming or going. After the storm, it is clear and it is night. I can see a full moon and the stars.

1. Write a question you have about the story.

____

2. Now reread the story. Write the answer to your question.

____

3. What does the narrator see in the sky at night?
a plane and a shooting star
a full moon and stars

TEKS **1.4 (B)** Ask relevant questions, seek clarification, and locate facts and details about texts.
RC-1 (B) Ask literal questions of the text.

Name ______________________________

To add **-er** or **-est** to words that end in **e**, drop the **e** and then add **-er** or **-est**.

cute + **er** = cut**er** That pup is **cuter** than this one.

cute + **est** = cut**est** The cat is the **cutest** of all.

When you add **-er** or **-est** to the end of a word, a new sound is added to the word.

Add -er or -est to each word. Then write the new word in the sentence.

1. His pet is ______________ than the wild cat.
   tame

2. The tree in the meadow is the ______________.
   large

3. My dad is the ______________ of all.
   brave

4. The ______________ bus should stop here.
   late

TEKS 1.3 (E) Read base words with inflectional endings.

Name ______________________________

Read the dictionary entries below.

middle halfway between two ends: We stood in the **middle** of the line.

mistake something thought or done incorrectly: I made one **mistake** on the spelling test.

protects to keep away from harm: The mother hen **protects** her eggs.

Use a word from the box to complete each sentence. You may use a word more than once.

1. Joan sat in the ______________ of her two friends.

2. The mother cat ______________ her babies.

3. Please draw a line down the ______________ of the paper.

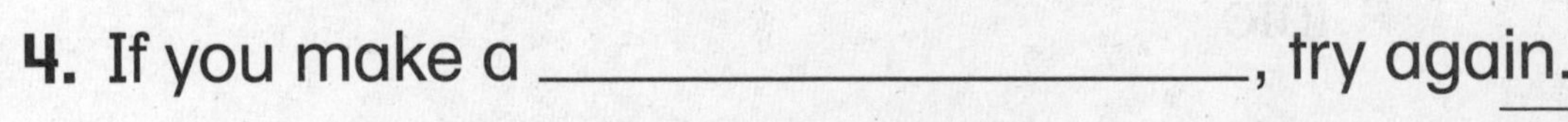

4. If you make a ______________, try again.

TEKS 1.6 (C) Determine what words mean from how they are used in a sentence, either heard or read. 1.6 (E) Use a dictionary to find words.

Name ____

As I read, I will pay attention to expression.

Miss Burns has a garden filled with herbs and flowers.
10 It makes Miss Burns smile. Her friends love the
19 garden, too.
21 Miss Burns is up early today because it is her birthday!
32 "It's my seventy-third!" says Miss Burns. "Who
40 will visit?"
42 Miss Burns checks her mail.
47 There is nothing in her box.
53 A blue bird chirps. Nothing else makes a peep.
62 Miss Burns picks an herb. It's green and curly.
71 She puts it in an urn. She feels a bit sad.
82 But then, lots of people came!
88 "Happy birthday!" they yelled. "We did not forget you!"
97 "You didn't!" Miss Burns cried. "I'm so glad!" 105

Comprehension Check

1. How old is Miss Burns?

2. What does the herb look like?

	Words Read	–	Number of Errors	=	Words Correct Score
First Read		–		=	
Second Read		–		=	

Name ______________________________

Nonfiction gives facts and information about a topic. It deals with a real-life subject.

Listen to the passage. Then answer the questions.

Have you ever looked up in the sky at night and seen a flash of light? You might think that it is a shooting star. In fact, shooting stars are not stars at all! You are seeing a *meteor*. Bits of dust and rocks from space fall toward Earth. When these bits get close, they hit the air around Earth. This makes the bits of dust and rock catch on fire. The burning bits are called meteors. The meteors leave a trail of light as they burn. This looks like a shooting star. The next time you see a shooting star, remember that it's not a shooting star, it's a meteor!

1. Put the events of a meteor in order by writing 1, 2, and 3.

_____ The meteors leave a trail of light.

_____ Bits of dust and rock from space hit the air around Earth and catch on fire.

_____ Bits of dust and rock from space fall toward Earth.

2. What is the main idea of this story? Circle the best answer.

Shooting stars are really meteors.
Shooting stars make pictures in the sky.

3. Circle one important fact that you learned about meteors.

TEKS **1.14 (A)** Restate the main idea, heard or read.
1.14 (B) Identify important facts in text, heard or read.
1.14 (C) Retell the order of events in a text by referring to the words.

Name ______________________________

Captions tell you facts about a photo or picture.

Read the captions. Then answer the questions.

On May 28, Paul and Mom paint his bedroom.

1. Who is in the picture? ______________________________

2. What are they doing? ______________________________

3. What is the date? ______________________________

On June 10, Pam and Joy make a sand castle at the beach.

4. Who are the children? ______________________________

5. What are the children doing? ______________________________

6. What is the date? ______________________________

TEKS 1.14 (D) Use text features to locate specific information in text.

Name ______________________________

A **Reading Log** tells about something that you read.

Read a fiction book or a nonfiction book every day this week. Then tell about what you read.

Title ______________________________

Author ______________________________

What I Read About ______________________________

Title ______________________________

Author ______________________________

What I Read About ______________________________

TEKS 1.12 Read independently for a sustained period of time.
1.19 (C) Write brief comments on literary or informational texts.

Name ___________________________

Together the letters **a** and **r** stand for the sound you hear in **car**. Listen for the **ar** sound in the word.

car 

Read the sentence. Then write the word that completes the sentence.

1. We can play in the ______________. yard yarn

2. The ______________ is far away. smart star

3. The ______________ has many teeth. start shark

4. Wheat grows on a ______________. farm barn

5. A ______________ is a fish. cart carp

6. Nana gave me a blue ______________. scar scarf

TEKS 1.3 (C) (vi) Use common syllabication patterns to decode words, including r-controlled vowel sounds.

Name ____

Practice

High-Frequency Words/Vocabulary

Read each sentence. Choose the word that completes the sentence. Circle the word.

1. Dan _____ like to play.

   would house

2. The number of balls _____.

   grew knew

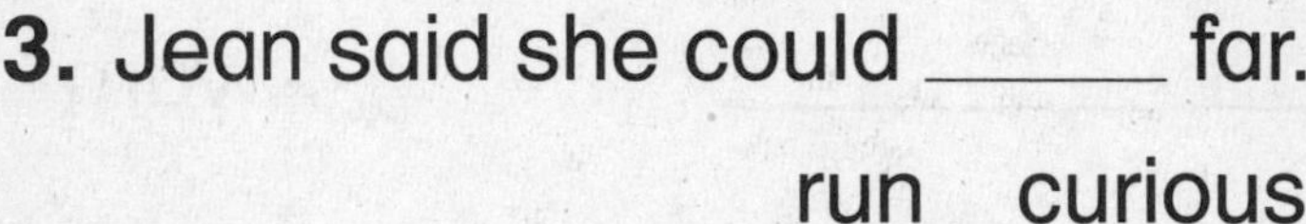

3. Jean said she could _____ far.

   run curious

4. "I _____ you were it!" she said.

   knew kind

5. Mike likes to look. He is _____.

   friends curious

6. Dean has another _____.

   idea knew

7. "I'm so glad we went to Dean's _____," said Mike.

   friends house

TEKS 1.3 (H) Identify and read at least 100 high-frequency words from a commonly used list.

Name ______________________________

As you read Meet Ben Franklin, fill in the Inference Chart.

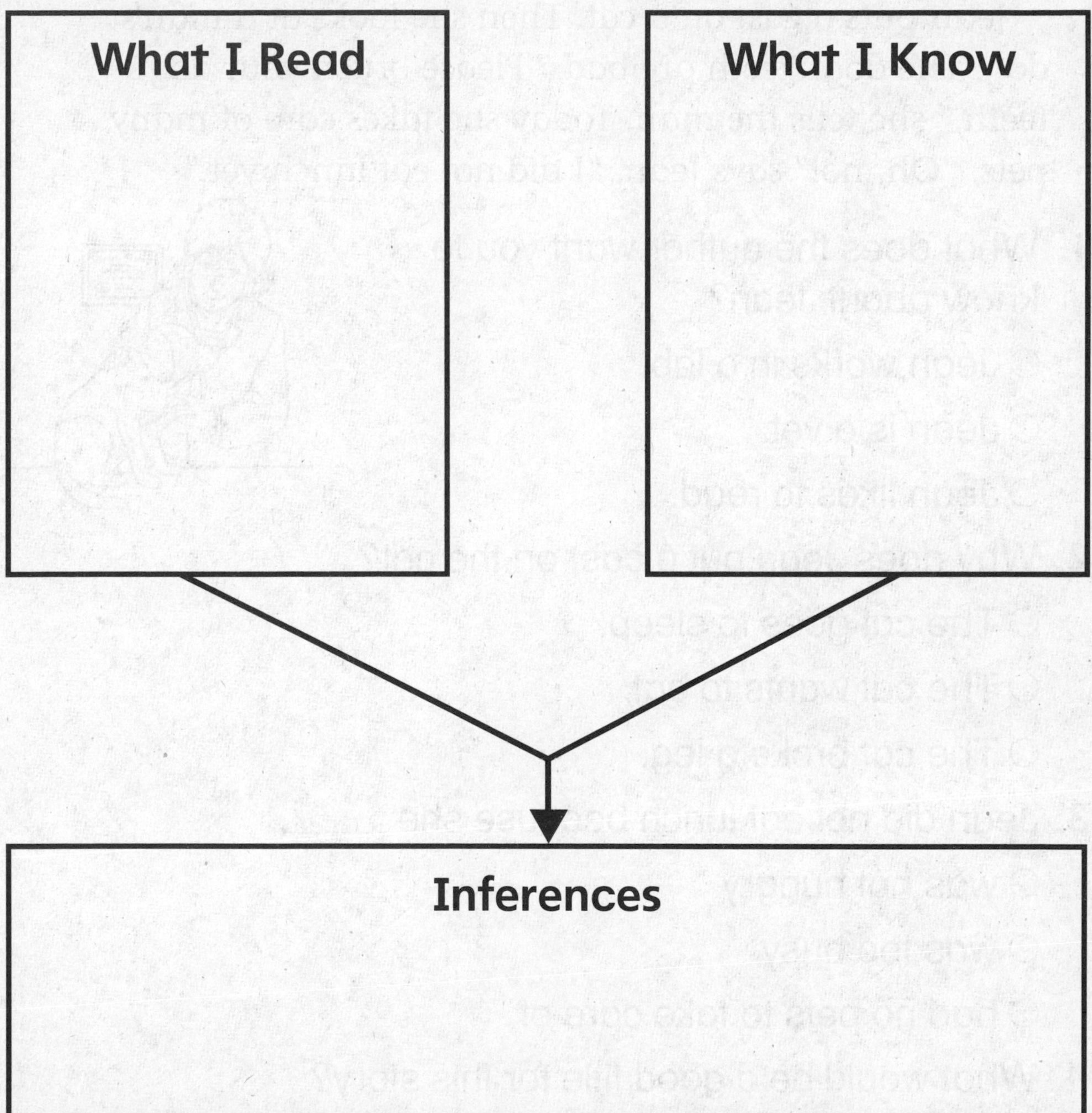

How does the Inference Chart help you identify important details in Meet Ben Franklin and make inferences about them?

TEKS 1.14 (B) Identify important facts or details in text, heard or read.

Practice

Comprehension: Make Inferences

Name ______________________________

Read the story. Then choose an answer to complete each sentence.

Jean puts a cast on a cat. Then she looks at a man's dog. The dog's teeth are bad. "Please brush your dog's teeth," she tells the man. Today she takes care of many pets. "Oh, no!" says Jean. "I did not eat lunch yet."

1. What does the author want you to know about Jean?
   - ○ Jean works in a lab.
   - ○ Jean is a vet.
   - ○ Jean likes to read.
2. Why does Jean put a cast on the cat?
   - ○ The cat goes to sleep.
   - ○ The cat wants to eat.
   - ○ The cat broke a leg.
3. Jean did not eat lunch because she _____.
   - ○ was not hungry
   - ○ was too busy
   - ○ had no pets to take care of
4. What would be a good title for this story?
   - ○ The Cat with the Broken Leg
   - ○ A Busy Day for Jean
   - ○ The Fast Dog

TEKS 1.14 (B) Identify important facts or details in text, heard or read.

Name ______________________________

Good readers **ask questions** about the story as they read. If they are not sure about something, they go back and reread the story to figure it out.

Read the story. Then answer the questions.

My name is Dr. Parker. I am a scientist. I work in a lab in a hospital. I use a microscope every day. A microscope is a good tool for a scientist. It makes very small things look much bigger. This helps me find out what is going on inside someone's body. I am like a detective for your body!

1. Write a question you have about the story.

____

____

2. Now reread the story. Write the answer to your question.

____

____

3. Dr. Parker uses a microscope to __________. Reread the story to find this information. Circle the best answer.

make small holes in the dirt
make dinner for his family
make small things look bigger

TEKS 1.4 (B) Ask relevant questions, seek clarification, and locate facts and details about texts.
RC-1 (B) Ask literal questions of the text.

Name ______________________________

An **abbreviation** is a short form of writing a longer word.

Look at these abbreviations.

Mister → Mr. Mistress → Mrs. Doctor → Dr.

A. Write the abbreviations for each word.

1. Doctor ____________

2. Mistress ____________

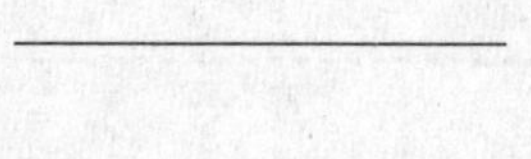

3. Mister ____________

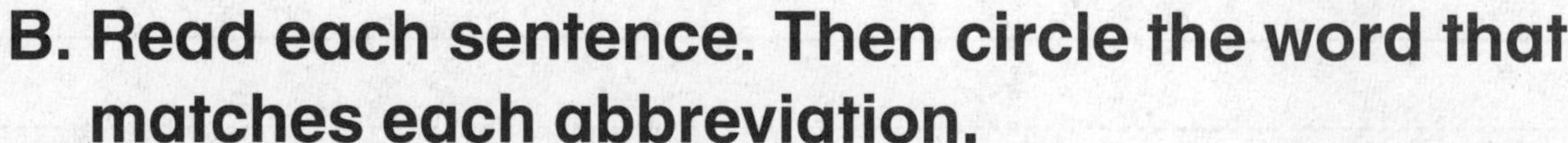

B. Read each sentence. Then circle the word that matches each abbreviation.

4. I will make a cake for <u>Mrs.</u> Smith.

Melissa Mistress Miss

5. <u>Dr.</u> Shin helps me when I'm sick.

Doctor Mistress Mister

6. We sent mail to <u>Mr.</u> Lee.

Doctor Saturday Mister

TEKS 1.6 (A) Identify words that name persons, places, or things (nouns).

Name ______________________________

A verb is a word that shows action. When a verb has the ending **-ed**, the action happened in the past. The **-ing** ending means the action is happening now. You can pick out the word parts of a verb to figure out its meaning.

Underline each word that has a word ending. Circle the base word. Write <u>now</u> if the action is happening now. Write <u>past</u> if the action happened in the past.

1. I am playing with my best friend. ______________

2. My cat climbed up the tree. ______________

3. Dad milked a cow. ______________

4. I am packing for my trip. ______________

5. We watched a good game. ______________

With a partner, find 7 nouns in the sentences.

TEKS 1.3 (E) Read base words with inflectional endings.
1.6 (A) Identify words that name actions (verbs) and words that name persons, places, or things (nouns).

Name ______________________________

As I read, I will pay attention to my rate.

My name is Carly. I'm a smart kid.
8 But I do NOT like the dark.
15 I know it will never harm me.
22 But I do NOT like the dark.
29 I try to sleep in the dark.
36 Mom says that I should. But it's so hard!
45 I do NOT like the dark.
51 Poor me! When I lay my head down,
59 I start to see shapes. I shout, "MOM!"
67 Mom says that the dark can play tricks!
75 It's just car lights shining on a scarf and a ball.
86 Still, it's hard to sleep. "I have a plan," Mom tells me.
98 Mom got me a night-light. She's so smart!
107 Now I can sleep through the night!
114 I am braver than ever before. 120

Comprehension Check

1. What happens when Carly lies down in the dark?

2. What does Mom do to help Carly?

	Words Read	–	Number of Errors	=	Words Correct Score
First Read		–		=	
Second Read		–		=	

TEKS 1.3 (I) Monitor accuracy of decoding.
1.5 Read aloud grade-level appropriate text with fluency and comprehension.

Name ______________________________

A **biography** tells the true story of a real person's life written by someone else.

Listen to the biography. Then answer the questions.

Isaac Newton was born long ago in England. He was a scientist and an inventor. He invented a telescope with a mirror to look at stars far away. He also thought about gravity. Gravity is the reason things fall down. It is also why we don't float off into space! Isaac Newton had so many new ideas that the queen of England made him a knight!

1. Circle the main idea of this biography.
   Isaac Newton was a scientist.
   The life of Isaac Newton.

2. Circle one fact you learned about Isaac Newton.

3. Put the events in order. Write 1, 2, and 3 on the lines.
   _____ The queen of England made Isaac Newton a knight.
   _____ Isaac Newton was born in England.
   _____ Isaac Newton was a scientist.

4. Is this story of Isaac Newton true or a fantasy? How can you tell?
   ____
   ____
   ____

TEKS 1.10 Determine whether a story is true or a fantasy and explain why.
1.14 (A) Restate the main idea, heard or read.
1.14 (B) Identify important facts in text, heard or read.
1.14 (C) Retell the order of events in a text by referring to the words.

Name ______________________________

Bold print points out important words.

Read the story. Then write the answer to each question below.

Ben Franklin was an **inventor**. He came up with ideas for many things that would help to make people's lives better. His **Franklin Stove** was a much safer way for people to burn wood for heat and for cooking. Even now we use a **lightning rod** to protect houses and ships from lightning. He gave his inventions away for **free**.

1. What is an inventor?

____

2. What did people use as a safer way to burn wood?

____

3. What does a lightning rod do?

____

TEKS 1.14 (D) Use text features to locate specific information in text.

Name ______________________________

A **Reading Log** tells about something that you read.

Read a fiction book or a nonfiction book every day this week. Then tell about what you read.

Title ______________________________

Author ______________________________

What I Read About ______________________________

Title ______________________________

Author ______________________________

What I Read About ______________________________

TEKS **1.12** Read independently for a sustained period of time.
1.19 (C) Write brief comments on literary or informational texts.

Name ______________________

The letters **or**, **oar**, and **ore** can stand for the middle sound in **horse**.

Circle the word that completes the sentence. Then write the word on the line.

1. The ______________ is in the barn.

porch horse roar

2. The ______________ is sharp.

storm stork thorn

3. They found ______________ in the mine.

ore store floor

4. The lamp has a new ______________.

cord fork soar

TEKS 1.3 (C) (vi) Use common syllabication patterns to decode words, including r-controlled vowel sounds.

Name ______________________________

A. Use words in the box to complete the sentences.

Their	cold	warm	great	know

1. A hat helps keep you ______________ in the winter.

2. Ice is very ______________.

3. We had a ______________ time at the party.

4. ______________ dog is black and white.

5. I ______________ how to tie my shoes.

B. Match the word to its meaning.

6. sound — very great; dangerous
7. predict — something you hear
8. extreme — to guess what will happen next

TEKS 1.3 (H) Identify and read at least 100 high-frequency words from a commonly used list.

Name ____________________

Practice

Comprehension: Compare and Contrast Chart

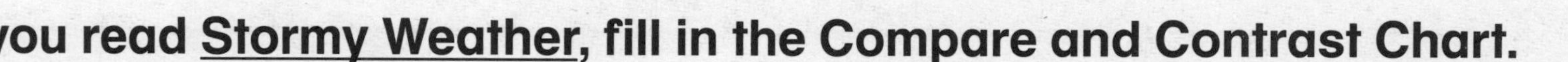

As you read Stormy Weather, fill in the Compare and Contrast Chart.

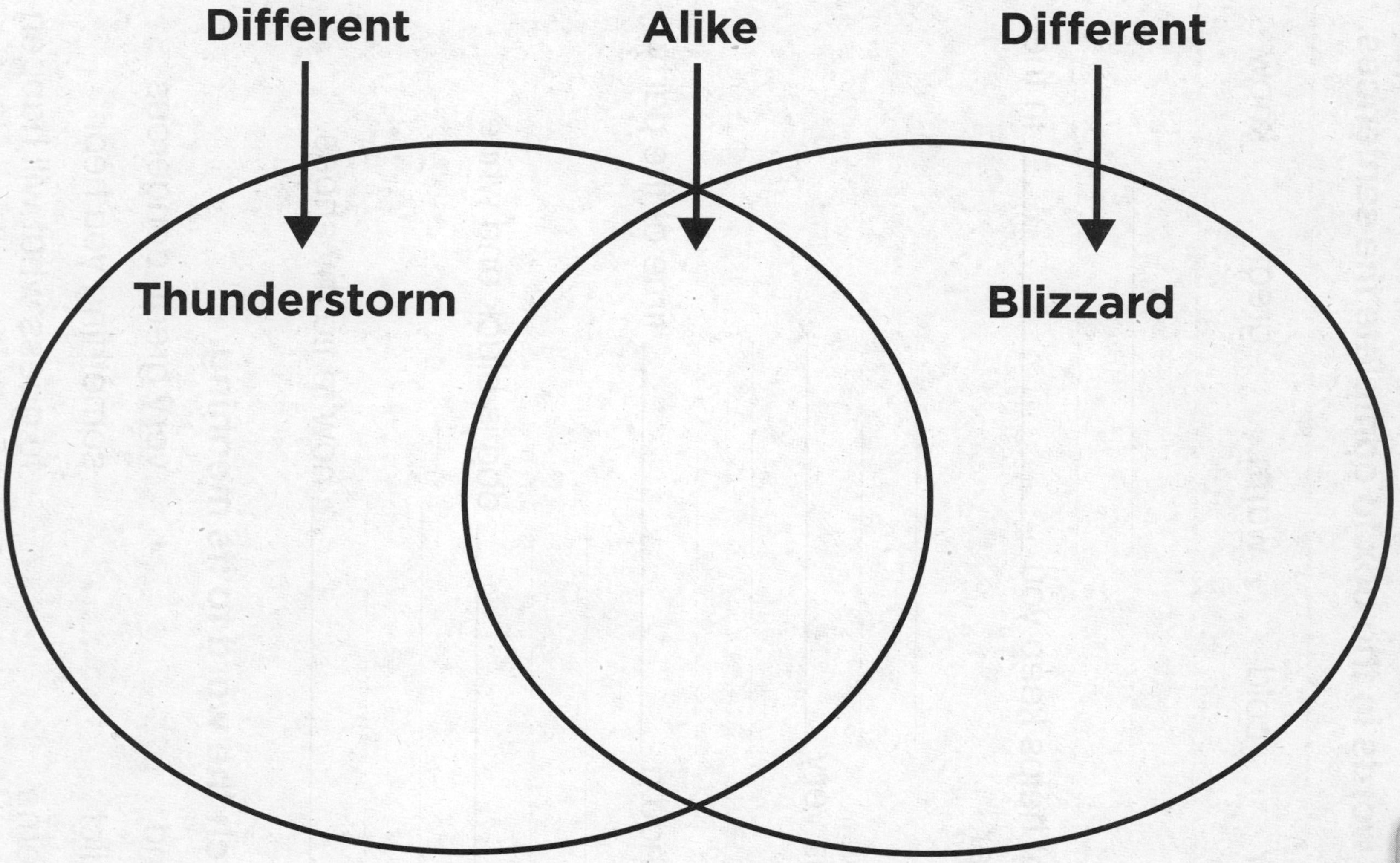
Different
Alike
Different
Thunderstorm
Blizzard

How does the Compare and Contrast Chart help you better understand Stormy Weather?

TEKS 1.14 (B) Identify important facts or details in text, heard or read.

Name ______________________________

When you **compare** two things, you see how they are the same.

When you **contrast** two things, you see how they are different.

Jay and May both like the water.
When it is warm, they go swimming.
When it is cool, Jay runs with a kite.
May digs holes.
If it rains, Jay takes a nap and May
has a snack.
When the weather is extreme, they both go home.

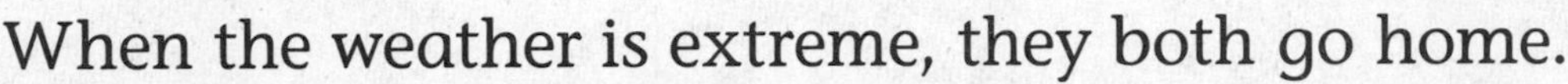

Compare Jay and May by listing how they are the same.

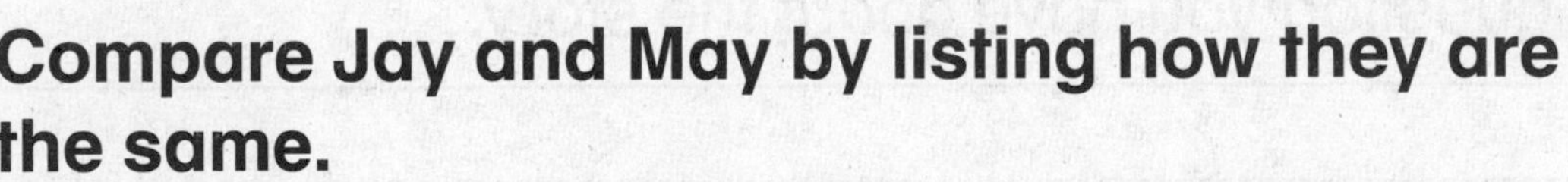

____

Contrast Jay and May by telling how they are different.

____

____

TEKS **1.14 (B)** Identify important facts or details in text, heard or read.

Name ______________________________

Good readers **ask questions** about the story as they read. If they are not sure about something, they go back and reread the story to figure it out.

Read the story. Then answer the questions.

Where I live, people say, "If you don't like the weather, wait five minutes." Yesterday, it was warm and sunny. I wore shorts and a T-shirt. My mom took us to the park. We rode our bikes. After dinner, we had a big storm. We saw lightning and thunder. The storm also made the weather change. It turned much colder. No more shorts!

1. Write a question you have about the story.

____

____

2. Now reread the story. Write the answer to your question.

____

____

3. What does the saying "If you don't like the weather, wait five minutes" mean? Circle the best answer.

If it is a nice day, you should go to the park.

The weather here changes a lot.

TEKS 1.4 (B) Ask relevant questions, seek clarification, and locate facts and details about texts. RC-1 (B) Ask literal questions of text. RC-1 (D) Make inferences about text.

Name ____________________

The letters **ea** can stand for the short **e** sound.

br**ea**d

Circle the word in each group that has the short *e* sound. Then write the word.

1. head	peach	bear	________
2. beach	spread	fear	________
3. bead	thread	deal	________
4. leaf	feast	sweat	________
5. weather	sea	each	________
6. neat	heavy	peanut	________

TEKS 1.3 (A) (v) Decode words in isolation by applying common letter-sound correspondences, including vowel digraphs.

Name ____________________

Practice

Vocabulary Strategy: Synonyms

Words with the same or almost the same meaning are **synonyms**. You can use a **dictionary** or a **thesaurus** to find synonyms. A thesaurus is a book that lists synonyms.

build to make something: Tim will **build** a house.

Synonyms: construct, make, create, form, and put together: Tim will **construct** a house.

Circle the two synonyms in each row that could complete the sentence.

1. That inventor has a clever _____.

broken invention creation

2. The robot can _____.

speak paper talk

3. The robot won the _____ in the contest.

prize box award

TEKS **1.6 (A)** Identify words that name actions (verbs) and words that name persons, places, or things (nouns). **1.6 (E)** Use a dictionary to find words.

Name ______________________________

As I read, I will pay attention to phrasing.

Mort is smaller than most of the children in
09 his class. So Mort's pal Cory named him Mort
18 the Short. Mort isn't good at running or other sports.
28 But he tries hard. He runs until he is worn out. His
40 mom yells, "Stop, Mort!"
44 At school, Miss Gore said, "We will have a Math
54 Bee." Mort's heart soared. He knew that he would win.
64 Mort did his math from morning until night. He added
74 up the numbers that his mom named. He got each
84 sum right!
86 But Cory gave Mort a hard time. "You won't win,"
96 she said. "I'm better at math than you are." That made
107 Mort study more than before! The Math Bee came.
116 Cory did well, but Mort got the Grand Prize! The class
127 roared. The prize was a big, round pin. Cory said, "Now I'll
139 have to name you Mort the Math Whiz!" 147

Comprehension Check

1. What made Mort feel happy?

2. Why did Cory give Mort the name Mort the Math Whiz?

	Words Read	–	Number of Errors	=	Words Correct Score
First Read		–		=	
Second Read		–		=	

TEKS 1.3 (I) Monitor accuracy of decoding.
1.5 Read aloud grade-level appropriate text with fluency and comprehension.

Name ______________________________

The **title** of a book is the name of the book. The **author** of a book writes the story. The **illustrator** makes the pictures. A **table of contents** tells what is inside the book.

Table of Contents

Look at the book cover and the Table of Contents. Then answer the questions.

1. Who wrote the book? ______________________

2. What is the title of the book? ______________________

3. Who made the pictures? ______________________

4. On what page would you read about Sam's Big Day? ______

TEKS 1.1 (F) Identify the information that different parts of a book provide.
1.14 (D) Use text features to locate specific information in text.

Name ______________________________

A **poem** often uses words that start with the same sound or words that rhyme. Poems try to use interesting words to paint a picture of something in the reader's mind.

Listen to the poem. Then answer the questions.

I love it when it's cold and gray.
That is my favorite kind of day.
The wind, it howls, and the rain, it falls.
The hail comes down like bouncing balls.
I can curl up with a book to read.
A cup of cocoa is all I need.
I feel safe and cozy in my bed like a nest.
A cold rainy day is really the best.

1. Circle the words that rhyme.

2. Complete the rhyming lines below to make your own weather poem.

____

On a ______________________________ day,

____

______________________________ is what I like to play.

TEKS 1.8 Respond to and use rhyme in poetry.

Name ________________________

Practice

Reading Log

A **Reading Log** tells about something that you read.

Read a fiction book or a nonfiction book every day this week. Then tell about what you read.

Title ________________________

Author ________________________

What I Read About ________________________

Title ________________________

Author ________________________

What I Read About ________________________

TEKS 1.12 Read independently for a sustained period of time.
1.19 (C) Write brief comments on literary or informational texts.

Name ______________________________

Use words from the box to complete the sentences.

cow	mouse	crown	clown
out	round	shout	

1. The king had a gold ____________ on his head.

2. The ball was red and ____________.

3. We can't go ____________ to play if it is raining.

4. The cat ran after the little ____________.

5. "Don't ____________ at me," yelled Ben.

6. The brown ____________ lives on a farm.

7. The funny ____________ had a red nose and big feet.

TEKS **1.3 (A) (vi)** Decode words in context by applying common letter-sound correspondences, including vowel diphthongs.

Name ______________________

Use the words from the box to complete the story.

against	fall	sure	below
yellow	orange	wondered	season

1. Look! Summer is gone. It is ________________.

2. It is the best ________________ of the year.

3. I am ________________ this will be a nice fall.

4. Leaves turn red, orange, and ________________.

5. I like the ________________ leaves better than the red or yellow ones.

6. She ________________ why the leaves fell.

TEKS **1.3 (H)** Identify and read at least 100 high-frequency words from a commonly used list.

Name ______________________________

As you read Happy Fall!, fill in the Sequence Chart.

First

↓

Next

↓

Then

↓

Last

How does the Sequence Chart help you visualize what happens in Happy Fall!?

TEKS **1.9 (A)** Retell a story's beginning, middle, and end with attention to the sequence of events.

Name ______________________________

The **sequence** tells what happens **first**, **next**, **then**, and **last** in story order.

Look at the pictures. Write what happens in each picture.

1. First, ______________________________.

2. Next, ______________________________.

3. Then, ______________________________.

4. Last, ______________________________.

TEKS 1.9 (A) Retell a story's beginning, middle, and end with attention to the sequence of events.

When you **summarize**, you retell the most important parts of a story in your own words.

Read the story. Then answer the questions.

This fall, we went to see my cousins in Vermont. We had to take an airplane to get there. It was very far away. We had fun while we were there. We hiked in the mountains. We found pretty leaves that were red, orange, brown, and yellow. We visited a maple syrup farm. We sure had a great time with our cousins. We were sad when it was time to go, but we know that they will come visit us soon. We can't wait to show them our part of Texas!

1. What would you show people who came to visit you?

____

____

2. Draw or write what happened in the beginning, middle, and end of the story.

beginning	middle	end

TEKS **1.9 (A)** Retell a story's beginning, middle and end with attention to the sequence of events.
RC-1 (E) Retell important events in stories in logical order.
RC-1 (F) Make connections to own experiences.

Name ____________________

Some words end with a silent **e**. The **e** in these words does not make a sound.

A. Circle the word that names each picture.

1. moose mound

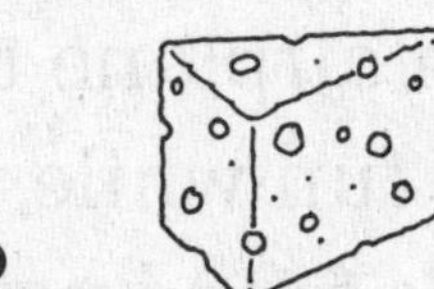

2. chick cheese

3. house horn

4. horse help

B. Use words from the box to complete each sentence. Write the word on the line.

please	blouse	choose	noise

5. It is kind to say ______________ and thank you.

6. A lot of ______________ can hurt your ears.

TEKS 1.3 (C) (iv) Use common syllabication patterns to decode words, including vowel-consonant-silent "e" words.

Name ______________________________

A **base word** is the word part that is left when you remove the **inflectional ending -ed** or **-ing**. You can use the base word to figure out the meaning of a word.

The teacher is **forming** the clay.
The base word is **form**.
Form means to give shape to something.

Write the base word.

1. moved moving ____________
2. listening listened ____________
3. crashed crashing ____________
4. whistled whistling ____________
5. baked baking ____________

TEKS 1.3 (E) Read base words with inflectional endings.

Name ______________________________

As I read, I will pay attention to questions in the passage and how they affect expression.

A little brown ant had a very big family. The ants seemed the
13 same, but the little brown ant was just a bit smaller than the rest.
27 When it gets cold in most places, ants gather food to be ready
40 for the winter. So all the ants set out fast! The little brown ant
54 was left alone. “Wait for me,” she shouted. But no one heard a
67 sound. When the little brown ant met up with the rest, they were
80 already on their way home. The little brown ant frowned. “All the
92 food is gone now. How will I eat?” The ant sat down to rest. She
107 saw something on the ground. The ant got closer. “Great!” she
118 cried loudly. “It’s a big, beautiful hunk of sweet cake. How will I
131 get it home from here? I am much too small.” The ant asked the
145 animals she met for help. Each one told her, “No. I will not
158 help.” “Well,” pouted the ant, “then I’ll have to do it myself!”
170 Crouching down, she lifted the cake up onto her head. Step by
182 step, the ant made it home! The cake would last all winter.
194 The ant had never felt so proud. 201

Comprehension Check

1. What did the little brown ant need for the winter?

2. Why did the little brown ant feel proud?

	Words Read	–	Number of Errors	=	Words Correct Score
First Read		–		=	
Second Read		–		=	

TEKS 1.3 (I) Monitor accuracy of decoding.
1.5 Read aloud grade-level appropriate text with fluency and comprehension.

Name ______________________________

A **biography** tells the true story of a real person's life written by another person.

Listen to the story. Then answer the questions.

Can you picture a snowflake in your mind? Then you should thank Wilson Bentley. He was the first man to take a picture of a snowflake. Wilson Bentley was born on a farm in 1865. When he was young, his mother gave him a microscope. He tried to use it to look at snowflakes, but they kept melting! He knew that he would have to take a picture. He tried and tried to take a picture, and after two years, he did it! The pictures helped him learn things about snow. He learned that every snowflake is different. In 1931, a book of his snowflake pictures was made. After that, people called Bentley "The Snowflake Man" because he loved to look at the snow.

1. Circle the main idea of this biography.
   Wilson Bentley did not like the winter.
   Wilson Bentley loved to study snow.

2. Circle one fact that you learned about Wilson Bentley.

3. Work with a partner. Tell what happened first, next, and last in Wilson Bentley's life.

TEKS
1.14 (A) Restate the main idea, heard or read.
1.14 (B) Identify important facts in text, heard or read.
1.14 (C) Retell the order of events in a text by referring to the words.

Name ______________________

Practice

Text Feature: Diagram

Look at the diagram of a fire truck. Use the words from the box to complete the diagram. Write the words of the correct labels.

ladder	light	hose	cab

1. ______________

2. ______________

3. ______________

4. ______________

TEKS 1.14 (D) Use text features to locate specific information in text.
1.24 (C) Record basic information in simple visual formats.

Name ______________________________

A **Reading Log** tells about something that you read.

Read a fiction book or a nonfiction book every day this week. Then tell about what you read.

Title ______________________________

Author ______________________________

What I Read About ______________________________

Title ______________________________

Author ______________________________

What I Read About ______________________________

TEKS **1.12** Read independently for a sustained period of time.
1.19 (C) Write brief comments on literary or informational texts.

Name ______________________________

Read the words. The letters **oy** and **oi** stand for the vowel sounds in b**oy** and b**oi**l.

boy **boil**

Read each sentence. Then complete the word by adding oi or oy.

1. The little child cried with j______ at the sight of the playful pups.

2. We will need more s______l for the new plants.

3. The little b______ laughed and ran toward his father.

4. Jen's new t______ toppled off the table and broke.

5. Mom has to put ______l in her car.

6. The water for our tea will b______l soon.

TEKS 1.3 (A) (vi) Decode words in context by applying common letter-sound correspondences, including vowel diphthongs.

Name ______________________________

Practice

High-Frequency Words/Vocabulary

Choose a word from the box to finish each sentence. Then write the word on the line.

wild	learn	enough	air	cub	eyes	open

1. The tiger ______________ has a sister.

2. Soon the cubs will be old ______________ to hunt in the ______________.

3. They will ______________ from their mother.

4. They like the night ______________.

5. Their ______________ see well at night.

6. The cubs ______________ their mouths and yawn.

TEKS 1.3 (H) Identify and read at least 100 high-frequency words from a commonly used list.

Name ____________________

As you read A Tiger Cub Grows Up, fill in the Sequence Chart.

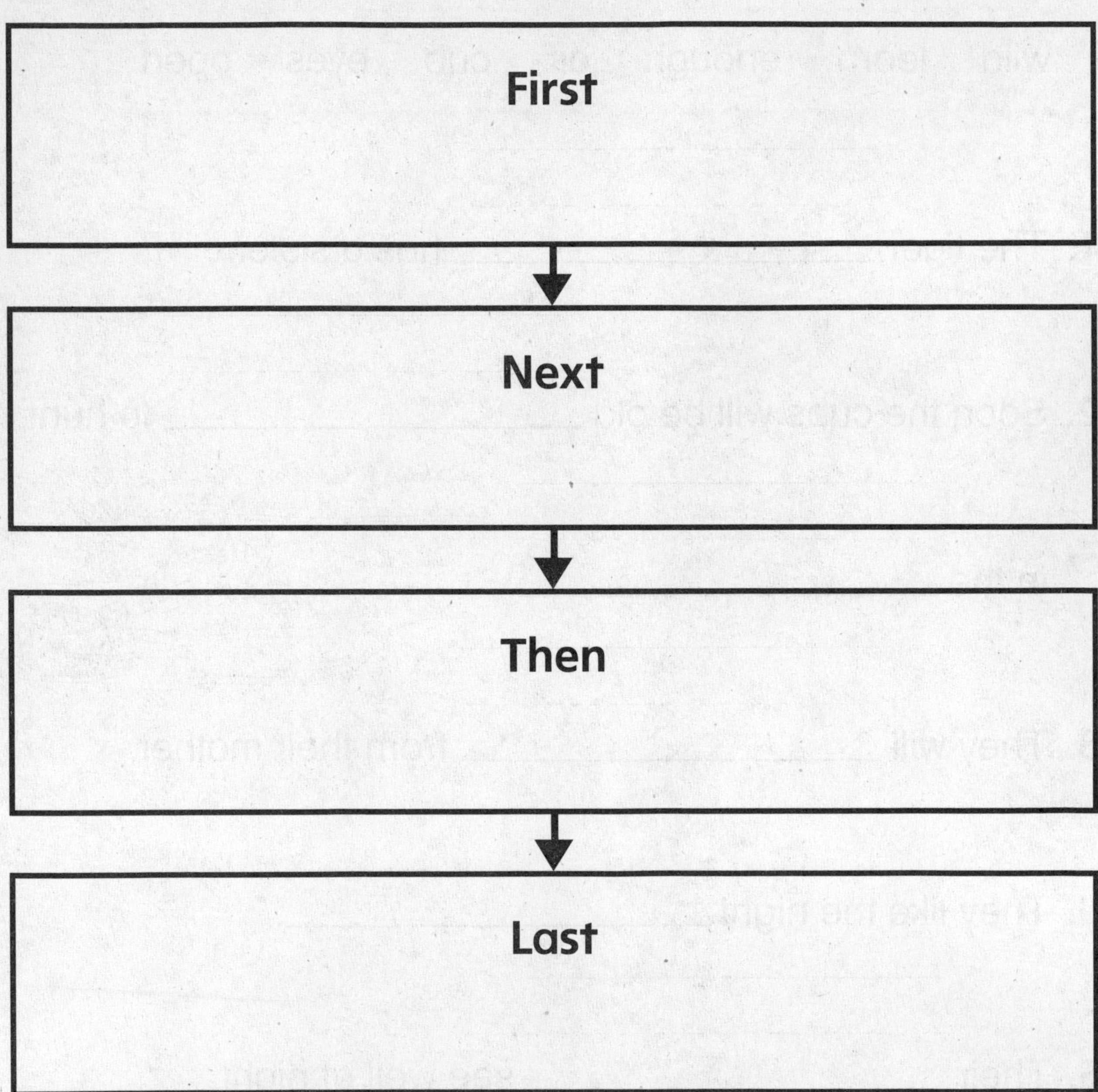

How does the Sequence Chart help you better understand the order of events in A Tiger Cub Grows Up?

TEKS **1.14 (C)** Retell the order of events in a text by referring to the words and/or illustrations.

Name ______________________________

The **sequence** tells what happens **first**, **next**, **then**, and **last** in a text.

Read the passage below. Then fill in the circle of the sentence that answers each question below.

When puppies are born, they are small. Their eyes stay closed, so they can't see. Their mother feeds them milk. When they are four weeks old, puppies open their eyes and can see. They also grow their teeth and learn to stand and walk. Next, they learn how to play. By the time they are 12 weeks old, puppies are ready to leave their mother. That's when they are ready to find a new home with you!

1. What happens first to puppies?

○ Puppies are born.

○ Puppies begin to open their eyes.

2. What happens next after puppies learn to walk?

○ Puppies grow their teeth.

○ Puppies learn how to play.

TEKS 1.14 (C) Retell the order of events in a text by referring to the words and/or illustrations.

Practice

Comprehension: Summarize (Nonfiction)

Name ______________________________

When you **summarize**, you retell the most important parts of a story in your own words.

Read the story. Then answer the questions.

A frog has many changes in its life. First, a mother frog lays soft round eggs in the water. The eggs stick together. Then the eggs hatch. Tadpoles come out. A tadpole has a head, a body, and a tail. Next, the tadpole begins to lose its tail. It grows legs in the front and back. Last, the tadpole becomes a frog. The frog lives both on land and in water. It will eat worms and insects. Some day the frog may lay eggs. What do you think will swim out?

1. Put the events of a frog's life in order. Write 1, 2, and 3.

__________ tadpole __________ frog __________ egg

2. What is the topic of this story? Circle the answer.

fish　　　　frogs

3. What is the main idea of the story?

A frog eats worms and insects.
A frog has many changes in its life.

4. Why do you think the author wrote this story?

to teach you about something funny
to teach you about something in real life

TEKS **1.4 (B)** Locate facts and details about stories. **1.13** Identify the topic and explain the author's purpose in writing about the text. **1.14 (A) (B) (C)** Restate the main idea, identify the important facts or details, and retell the order of events in an informational text. **RC-1 (E)** Retell important events in stories in logical order.

Name ______________________

A **prefix** is a word part you can add to the beginning of a base word to change the meaning of the word.

The prefix **re-** means **again**: **re** + pack = **re**pack

The prefix **un-** means **not** or **the opposite**: **un** + pack = **un**pack

Write the meaning of each of the following two-syllable words:

1. reuse ______________
2. refill ______________
3. unload ______________
4. unsafe ______________
5. remake ______________
6. untrue ______________

TEKS 1.3 (B) Combine sounds from letters and common spelling patterns to create recognizable words.

Name ______________________________

Context clues are words that help you figure out the meaning of a new word. Context clues may be found in the same sentence or in nearby sentences.

Use context clues to figure out the meaning of the underlined word. Fill in the correct circle.

1. The man displays the fruit. He wants to set the melon on the shelf.

○ throws away

○ shows or sets out

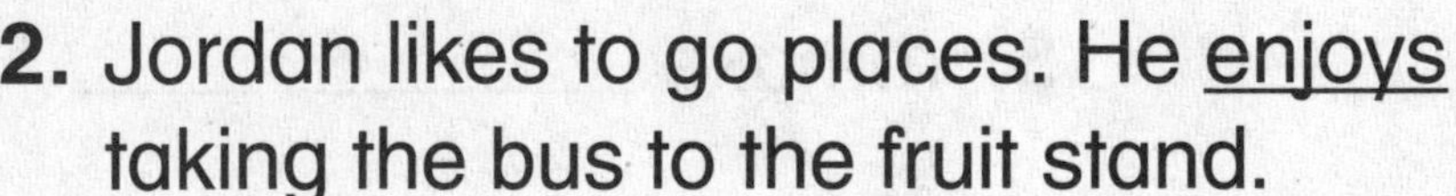

2. Jordan likes to go places. He enjoys taking the bus to the fruit stand.

○ likes

○ twists

3. Jordan's mom likes to relax at the park. She likes to sit and read.

○ finish quickly

○ rest

TEKS 1.6 (C) Determine what words mean from how they are used in a sentence, heard or read.

Name ______________________________

As I read, I will pay attention to phrasing in the passage.

Farmer Roy worked in Illinois. He had a nice house and
11 farm. Roy raised fat hogs. Roy's hogs sure made him joyful.
22 But Roy did not enjoy one thing. His hogs OINKED and
33 OINKED! The noise kept Roy up all night! So Roy sold his
45 hogs to a farmer across town.
51 "My farm has rich soil," said Roy. "I'll learn to raise corn."
63 Roy planted his yellow corn. Soon it was 10 feet high!
74 The next week it reached 30 feet!
81 Roy got rich, thanks to those noisy hogs.
89 "Oh, boy! I'm lucky," he said. "Illinois has some fine soil
100 for fine corn"! 103

Comprehension Check

1. Describe Farmer Roy's hogs.

2. How did Farmer Roy get rich?

	Words Read	–	Number of Errors	=	Words Correct Score
First Read		–		=	
Second Read		–		=	

TEKS **1.3 (I)** Monitor accuracy of decoding.
1.5 Read aloud grade-level appropriate text with fluency and comprehension.

Name ______________________________

Nonfiction gives facts and information about a topic.

Listen to the story. Then answer the questions.

The ostrich is an amazing animal. It is the biggest bird in the world. Like other birds, it has a beak and feathers and lays eggs. Unlike most other birds, the ostrich can't fly. It has two long, strong legs to help it run very fast. An ostrich begins big, too. An ostrich egg is as heavy as 24 chicken eggs! An ostrich grows to be 7 to 9 feet tall. That is taller than most people are. It has the biggest eye of any animal on land. Ostriches eat plants. They can also eat insects and small animals such as lizards. They also eat sand and small rocks to help grind up their food.

1. What would be a good title for this story? Circle the best answer.
   Ostriches Live in the Desert
   Ostriches Are Big, Amazing Birds
   Plant-Eating and Animal-Eating Animals

2. Circle two facts that you learned about ostriches.

3. Work with a partner. Tell what you learned about first, next, and last in this passage.

TEKS 1.14 (A) Restate the main idea, heard or read.
1.14 (B) Identify important facts in text, heard or read.
1.14 (C) Retell the order of events in a text by referring to the words.

Name ________________________________

Poets often use words in fun and interesting ways. The sounds of words can help express their meaning.

Read the poem. Circle the sound words in each verse. Then write your own poem on the lines.

Bow-Wow

Bow-wow says the dog,
Mew, mew says the cat,
Grunt, grunt goes the hog,
And squeak goes the rat.

Whoo-oo says the owl,
Caw, caw says the crow,
Quack, quack says the duck,
And what cuckoos say, you know.

Name ____________________

A **Reading Log** tells about something that you read.

Read a fiction book or a nonfiction book every day this week. Then tell about what you read.

Title ____________________

Author ____________________

What I Read About ____________________

Title ____________________

Author ____________________

What I Read About ____________________

TEKS **1.12** Read independently for a sustained period of time.
1.19 (C) Write brief comments on literary or informational texts.

Name ______________________________

The letters **oo** can stand for two sounds. The first is the same as the middle sound in g**oo**d. The second is a long **u** sound, like the middle sound in m**oo**n. The long **u** sound can also be spelled in other ways.

bl**ue** | n**ew** | t**u**b**e** | s**ou**p

A. Change one letter in good to write two new words that have the same oo sound.

good ______________ ______________

B. Read the first word. Then circle another words in the line with the same long u sound.

1. glue	top	clue	bag
2. threw	flew	scarf	flower
3. group	jar	fence	you
4. cube	disk	cup	tube
5. spoon	food	walk	paper

TEKS 1.3 (A) (ii) (10); (v) (1) (2) (13) Decode words in isolation by applying common letter-sound correspondences, including single letters (vowels) and including vowel digraphs including oo as in foot, oo as in moon, and ew.

Name ______________________________

Practice

High-Frequency Words/Vocabulary

mother	four	always	firm
father	love	supposed	

Use words from the box to complete the sentences.

1. My mom is my ______________________.

2. My dad is my ______________________.

3. We ______________________ each other.

4. We ______________________ help each other.

5. We have ______________________ cats.

6. I am ______________________ to be good.

7. Sometimes they are ______________________ with me.

TEKS **1.3 (H)** Identify and read at least 100 high-frequency words from a commonly used list.

Name ____________________

As you read Olivia, fill in the Fantasy and Reality Chart. Use words from the story.

Reality	Fantasy
What Could Happen?	**What Could Not Happen?**

How does the Fantasy and Reality Chart help you better understand Olivia?

TEKS 1.10 Determine whether a story is true or a fantasy and explain why.

Name ______________________________

Reality is something that could be true or that could really happen.

Fantasy is something that could not really happen.

Circle the sentences that show reality. Then underline the sentences that are fantasy.

1. A pig puts on a dress.

2. A pig paints.

3. A pig sleeps.

4. A pig goes to school.

5. A pig has a pet cat.

6. A pig sits in the mud.

7. A pig reads a book.

8. A pig has a mother.

TEKS 1.10 Determine whether a story is true or a fantasy and explain why.

Name ______________________________

As you read, use words to help you **visualize**, or make pictures in your mind, what you are reading about.

Read the story. Then answer the questions.

"I do not want to cook tonight," said my father. "Let's go out to eat!" We all cheered. We went to my favorite place. I love to eat Mexican food! First, we had some chips. The salsa that came with them was spicy. I drank some milk. Next, out came our meal. I had a big plate of beef tacos. I really liked the cheese. My mom had a salad. My dad had beans and rice. I love to go out to eat.

1. Reread the story. Circle the words that helped you visualize the people, places, and things.

2. Draw or write about a time when you went out to eat.

TEKS RC-1 (C) Monitor and adjust comprehension.
RC-1 (F) Make connections to own experiences.

Name ______________________________

When **'s** is added to a word, it means that something belongs to that person or thing.

Circle the correct word and write it on the line.

1. This is ______________________ ball.

   Olivia   Olivia's

2. This is ______________________ shirt.

   Jan's   Jan

3. This is ______________________ bone.

   Perry   Perry's

4. This is the ______________________ milk.

   cat's   cat

5. This is ______________________ pencil.

   Mom   Mom's

TEKS 1.6 (C) Determine what words mean from how they are used in a sentence, either heard or read.

Name ___________________________

pretends plays or makes believe: Danny **pretends** he is an astronaut.

vanished disappeared: The sun **vanished** when the clouds came out.

observes sees or notices: A scientist **observes** things under a microscope.

inspecting looking at carefully: Mom is **inspecting** the house for dust.

Use a word from above to complete each sentence.

1. Kate thinks Matt ____________ from the room!

2. She is ____________ the room for clues.

3. He hides behind the toy box and ____________ to be invisible.

4. Kate ____________ many clues. She solves the mystery of the missing brother!

TEKS 1.6 (C) Determine what words mean from how they are used in a sentence, either heard or read.

Name ______________________________

Practice

Fluency: Echo Read: Phrasing

As I read, I will pay attention to phrasing.

Mrs. Booth's room is planning a "Let's Find Out Day."
10 We are sitting in a small group. We will tell what we
22 plan to do. Joe will bring flowers that he grew.
32 Joy will show her drawings of clouds and blue sky.
42 I'll bring my new pet mouse, Sue. She is good at
53 learning to crawl in a maze. I trained her to find food.
65 The next day, I take Sue to school in a huge box.
77 But when I open the box, she is gone!
86 We check and recheck the classroom.
92 "Come on, Sue," I yell. "Don't spoil my plan."
101 The kids help me look. Our "Let's Find Out" day
111 is renamed "Let's Find Sue" day!
117 I don't think we will ever find Sue.
125 Now I see June point. June finds my mouse!
134 The day turns out fine. But now Mrs. Booth will
144 rethink the new rule. No more pets in school. 153

Comprehension Check

1. What is Sue learning to do?

2. Who finds Sue?

	Words Read	–	Number of Errors	=	Words Correct Score
First Read		–		=	
Second Read		–		=	

TEKS 1.3 (I) Monitor accuracy of decoding.
1.5 Read aloud grade-level appropriate text with fluency and comprehension.

Name ______________________________

A **fantasy** is a story that blends make-believe things with things that could be true. In a fantasy, the characters might be animals that talk.

Think about "Hilda Must Be Dancing." Then answer the questions.

1. How do you know that this story is a fantasy?

   a. The characters are people.

   b. The characters are animals that talk.

2. Why do the other animals want Hilda to take up another hobby?

   a. The ground shakes when she dances.

   b. A crowd gathers to watch her dance.

3. Work with a partner. Tell what happened first, next, and last in "Hilda Must Be Dancing."

4. Dancing is Hilda's favorite hobby. Write a sentence about your favorite hobby.

____

____

TEKS **1.7 (A)** Connect the meaning of a well-known story or fable to personal experiences.
1.9 (A) Describe the plot (problem/solution) and retell a story's beginning, middle, and end with attention to the sequence of events.
1.9 (B) Describe characters in a story and the reasons for their actions and feelings.

Name ______________________

Practice

Text Feature: Maps

A **map** is a drawing. It shows where places are.

Look at the map. Then answer the questions.

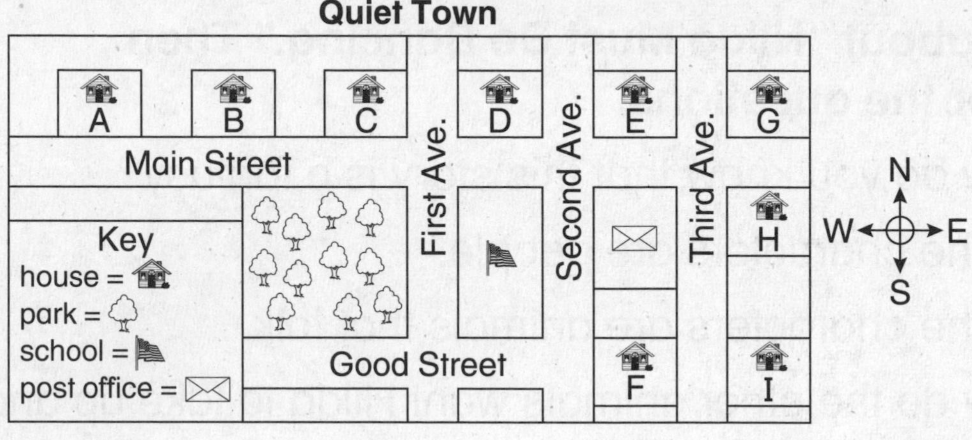

1. How many houses are in Quiet Town? ______

2. How many post offices are in Quiet Town? ______

3. If you lived in house A, what street would you walk on to get to the park? ______

4. A new swingset was just put next to the school. What would be a good symbol for the swingset? Draw your answer next to the map.

TEKS 1.15 (B) Explain the meaning of specific signs and symbols.

Name ____________________

A **Reading Log** tells about something that you read.

Read a fiction book or a nonfiction book every day this week. Then tell about what you read.

Title ____________________

Author ____________________

What I Read About ____________________

Title ____________________

Author ____________________

What I Read About ____________________

TEKS 1.12 Read independently for a sustained period of time.
1.19 (C) Write brief comments on literary or informational texts.

Name ______________________________

The letters **au**, **aw**, and **augh** stand for the vowel sound in P**au**l, p**aw**, and t**augh**t. The letter **a** in t**a**ll also makes this vowel sound.

Circle the word that answers each riddle.

1. A mouse is this size?

   What is it? small big

2. I grabbed with my claw.

   What did I do? call caught

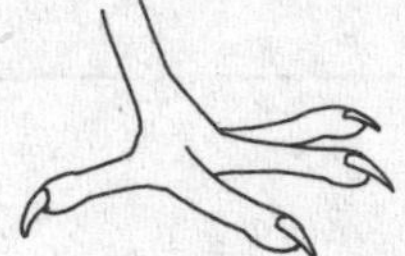

3. When you are dirty, do this.

   What is it? fix wash

4. I like to do this in art class.

   What is it? draw drink

5. The girl on the phone did this.

   What is it? filled called

TEKS 1.3 (A) (v) Decode words in context and in isolation by applying common letter-sound correspondences, including vowel digraphs.

Name ______________________________

Use a word from the box to complete each sentence.

early	along	suddenly	errand
nothing	thought	instead	

1. We woke up ____________ this morning.

2. We did an ____________ for Mom.

3. There was ____________ in the rice jar.

4. Mr. Ford ____________ he had no rice.

5. He gave us beans ____________.

6. ____________, it started to rain.

7. Mr. Ford told us to run ____________.

TEKS 1.3 (H) Identify and read at least 100 high-frequency words from a commonly used list.

Name ______________________________

Practice

Comprehension: Inference Chart

As you read Whistle for Willie, fill in the Inference Chart. Use words from the story.

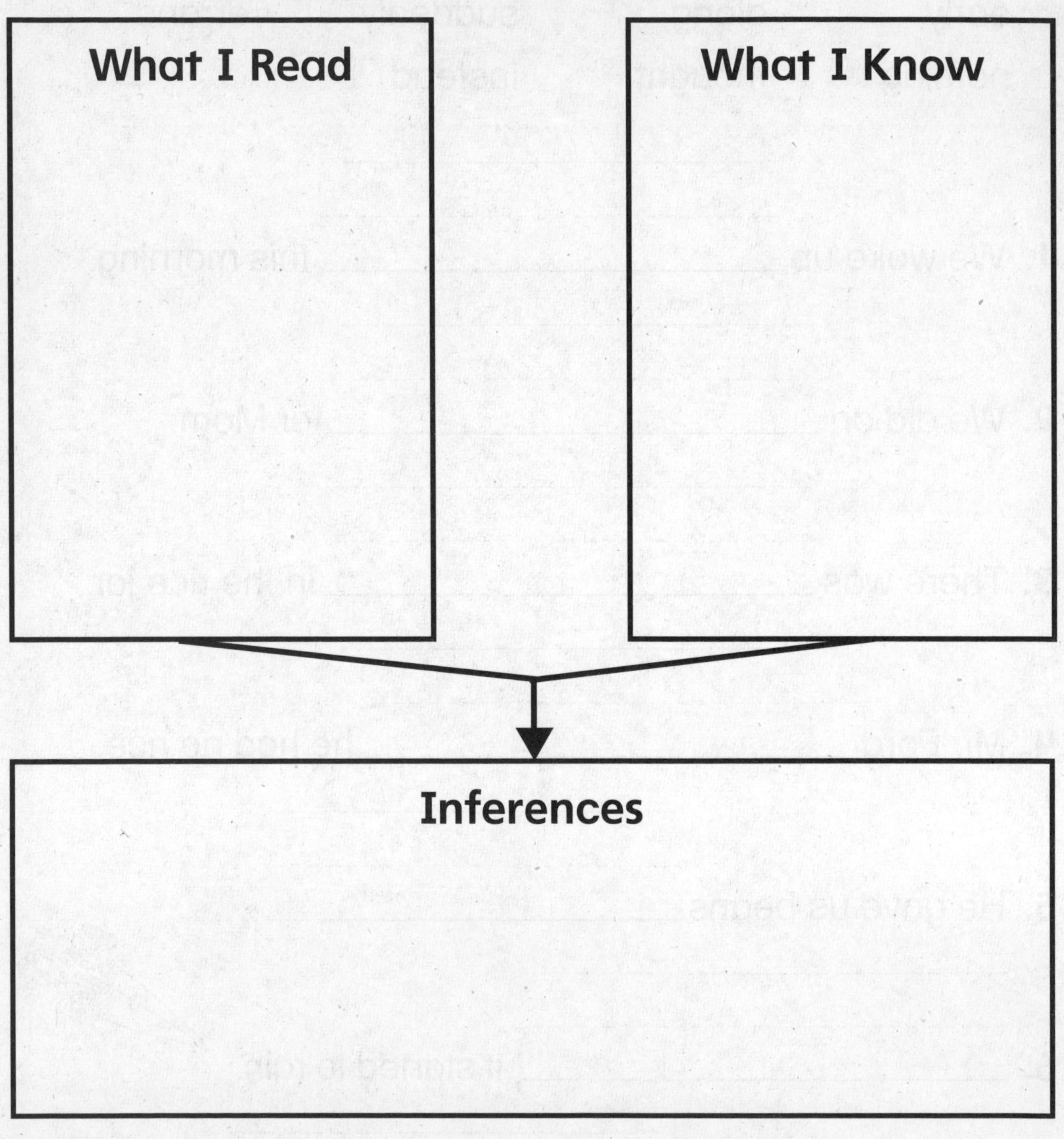

How does the Inference Chart help you better understand Whistle for Willie?

TEKS 1.9 (B) Describe characters in a story and the reasons for their actions and feelings.

Name ________________________________

Look at the picture. Use what you already know. Then underline the sentence that is true.

1.

Saul likes to play ball.

Saul wins the race.

Saul likes to ride his bike.

2.

I can play catch.

I can see far away.

I can sing and dance.

3.

I can play a game.

I can help Dad.

I can read a good book.

4.

The water is fun.

The water is not deep.

The water is too cold.

5.

I don't like to help.

I can help Mom make pancakes.

I don't know how to make pancakes.

TEKS **1.9 (B)** Describe characters in a story and the reasons for their actions and feelings.

Name ________________________________

As you read, use words to help you **visualize**, or make pictures in your mind, what you are reading about.

A. Read the first part. Answer the question.

It was a rainy day. I was very bored. Mom said she had an idea. She wanted to make ants on a log for us to eat. "Ants? Yuck!" I said. But Mom said it was a cool treat.

1. Draw what you think ants on a log would look like.

B. Read the rest of the story. Answer the question.

First, Mom cut some celery. The celery looked like logs. Then I spread cream cheese down the middle of each log. Last, I added raisins on top. They looked like ants! That's why this treat is called ants on a log!

2. Look at the picture you drew. Was the treat what you had pictured? Why or why not?

____

____

TEKS RC-1 (C) Monitor and adjust comprehension.

Name ______________________________

Some pronouns go before a noun. Some stand alone.

This is **my** book. That pen is **mine**.

Use a pronoun from the box to complete the sentences. Use the underlined words as clues.

my	mine	your	her	hers	yours

1. This flute belongs to <u>Patty</u>. This flute is __________.

2. That kite belongs to <u>me</u>. That kite is __________.

3. This is <u>Lisa's</u> pet. This is __________ pet.

4. This kitten belongs to <u>you</u>. This kitten is __________.

TEKS 1.6 (C) Determine what words mean from how they are used in a sentence, either heard or read. 1.20 (A) (iv) Understand and use the following parts of speech in the context of reading, writing, and speaking: pronouns.

Name ______________________________

Context clues are words that help you figure out the meaning of a new word. Context clues may be found in the same sentence or in nearby sentences.

Fill in the circle next to the correct meaning of the bold word. Use the underlined context clues to figure out the meaning of each word.

1. The girls are giggling and **fooling** around on the stage.

   ○ acting silly ○ cleaning

2. They are in a show about stars and planets in **space**.

   ○ the beach ○ a place where astronauts travel

3. The big **helmet** hides most of Seta's face.

   ○ boots ○ something that protects a person's head

4. Maria fell down. Her moon rocks **tumbled** off the stage.

   ○ dropped ○ dug

5. "These space boots make it hard to feel the **earth** under my feet," said Seta.

   ○ cold water ○ ground; also the planet where we live

TEKS 1.6 (C) Determine what words mean from how they are used in a sentence, either heard or read.

Name ______________________________

As I read, I will pay attention to the phrasing.

Dawn always played ball with Paul on the lawn.
09 One day, Paul threw the ball high
16 and Dawn caught it.
20 Then Dawn threw the small ball too hard.
28 It wasn't her fault.
32 It caused the ball to go past Paul.
40 Dawn saw it go in the street.
47 Paul ran to scoop up the ball. Dawn called,
56 "No, Paul! Don't get the ball! Stay on the lawn!"
66 Dawn ran to stop Paul. She grabbed Paul's legs
75 and stuck to him like glue.
81 Dawn made Paul fall.
85 Mother and Father ran outside.
90 "Nice job, Dawn!" Mother said. "You saved Paul!"
98 "I love Paul," said Dawn.
103 "I always want him to be safe." 110

Comprehension Check

1. What were Dawn and Paul doing?

2. How did Dawn save Paul?

	Words Read	–	Number of Errors	=	Words Correct Score
First Read		–		=	
Second Read		–		=	

Name ______________________________

Folk tales are stories that have been told for many years. They often include animals that talk and act like people.

Think about the folk tale "Turtle's Race with Beaver." Then circle the best answer to each question.

1. The folk tale begins with the words "Long ago." What does that tell you about the story?

   a. The story has been told many times.

   b. This story happens today.

2. How do you know that "Turtle's Race with Beaver" is a folk tale?

   a. The story takes place in a pond.

   b. The animals talk and act like people.

3. What lesson did Beaver learn?

   a. Never race a turtle.

   b. Always share with others.

4. The folk tale ends with Beaver living "happily through all seasons to come." What does that tell you about the story?

   a. Beaver learned a lesson and was happy.

   b. Beaver had to leave the pond but lived a long time.

TEKS **1.7 (B)** Explain the function of recurring phrases in traditional folk and fairy tales.

Name ____________________

A **list** is a series of things written in a certain order.

Dogs can do these jobs:

1. look for clues
2. help the blind
3. pull a sled

4. watch sheep

Read the list. Draw a line to the answer.

1. Which dog helps the blind?
2. Which dog looks for clues?
3. Which dog watches sheep?
4. Which dog pulls a sled?

TEKS 1.14 (D) Use text features to locate specific information in text.

Name ______________________________

A **Reading Log** tells about something that you read.

Read a fiction book or a nonfiction book every day this week. Then tell about what you read.

Title ______________________________

Author ______________________________

What I Read About ______________________________

Title ______________________________

Author ______________________________

What I Read About ______________________________

TEKS 1.12 Read independently for a sustained period of time.
1.19 (C) Write brief comments on literary or informational texts.

Name ______________________________

When **re**- or **un**- is added to the beginning of a word, it changes the meaning of the word.

re- = again **un**- = not

When **re**- or **un**- is added to the beginning of a word, the word gets another syllable.

Add re- or un- to each of the base words below. Write the words on the lines.

1. check ______________
2. hurt ______________
3. safe ______________
4. play ______________
5. read ______________
6. use ______________
7. fair ______________
8. heat ______________

TEKS 1.3 (D) Decode words with common spelling patterns.

Name ______________________________

Use the words in the box to complete each sentence.

only	laugh	goes	build	ordinary	interesting

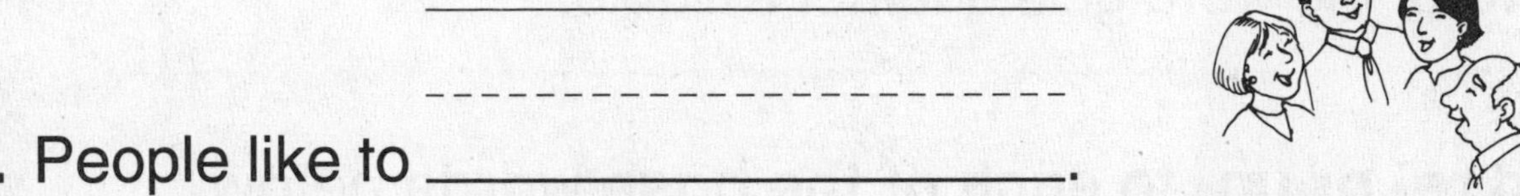

1. People like to ______________.

2. It eats ______________ the leaf.

3. She ______________ in.

4. This bird is ______________.

5. This bird is more ______________.

6. Let's watch the bird ______________ a nest.

TEKS 1.3 (H) Identify and read at least 100 high-frequency words from a commonly used list.

Name ______________________________

As you read Cool Jobs, fill in the Classify and Categorize Chart. Use words from the selection.

Classify and Categorize	
Jobs to Make Things	**Jobs That Help**

How does the Classify and Categorize Chart help you better understand Cool Jobs?

Name ______________________________

Write A if the sentence or sentences tell how two or more things are alike. Write D if the sentence or sentences tell how two or more things are different.

1. Ted has a black dog. May has a black cat. ______

2. Sam likes to sing and Mike likes to dance. ______

3. Dana and Karen have on blue pants. ______

4. Cara's flowers are red. Nia's flowers are pink. ______

5. Both toys are broken. ______

6. All of the babies are small. ______

TEKS 1.14 (B) Identify important facts or details in text, heard or read.

Name ______________________________

If a story is not clear as you read it, ask yourself questions about it. Then **reread** the story. Look for clues to answer your questions.

Read the story. Then answer the questions.

A Dentist's Job

A dentist helps take care of your teeth. A dentist looks for cavities in your teeth. The dentist may use an x-ray machine. The x-ray takes a picture of the inside of your teeth. A cavity will appear as a dark spot on the x-ray picture. A dentist takes care of the cavity and makes your teeth healthier. You can help a dentist by brushing and flossing your teeth twice a day. Try to brush in the morning and at night.

1. Write a question that you have about a dentist's job.

____

2. Reread the story. Look for clues to answer your question.

____

____

TEKS **1.4 (B)** Ask relevant questions, seek clarification, and locate facts and details about stories and other texts. **1.4 (C)** Monitor comprehension, making corrections when that understanding breaks down. **RC-1 (C)** Monitor and adjust comprehension.

Name ________________________________

The letters ***air***, ***are***, and ***ear*** can make the same sound.

ch**air** sp**are** pe**ar**

Write the words from the box that have the same vowel sound and spelling as the name of the picture.

fair	bear	dare	wear	pair	share

1. 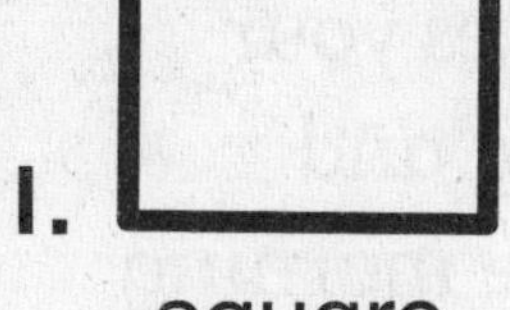
square
______________ ______________
______________ ______________

2. 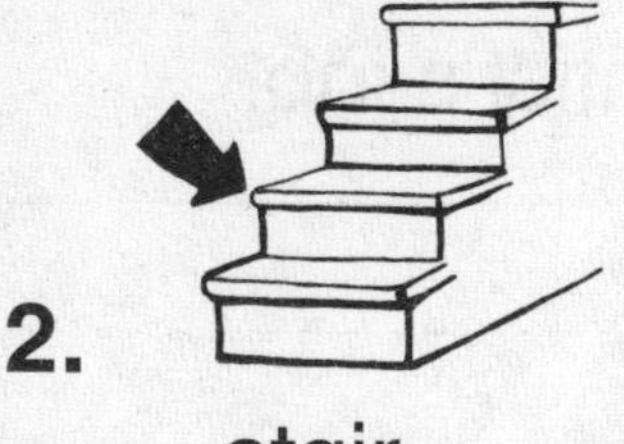
stair
______________ ______________
______________ ______________

3. 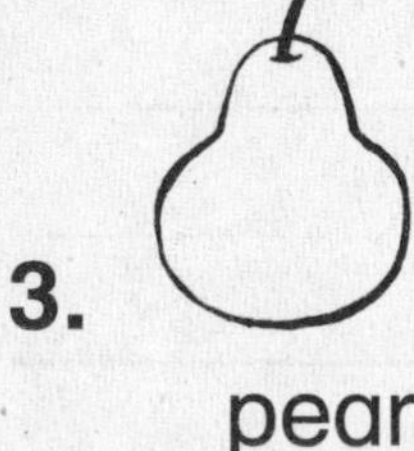
pear
______________ ______________
______________ ______________

TEKS 1.3 (D) Decode words with common spelling patterns.

Name ______________________________

A **dictionary** is a book that gives the meaning of words. Some words have more than one meaning.

Read the definitions below.

flyer 1. a person who flies aircraft: The **flyer** did tricks in the small plane. **2.** a sheet of paper with information: The **flyer** gave the time and place of the sale.

model 1. a person who shows off clothes or other things: The **model** came down the runway in a beautiful dress. **2.** a small example of something: Jim built a ship **model**.

Choose the correct definition for the word. Fill in the circle.

1. flyer ○ paper with words ○ fix a roof
2. flyer ○ place in line ○ person in a plane
3. model ○ sit down ○ show off clothes
4. model ○ small example ○ sandy beach

Use a word from above in a sentence.

____

TEKS 1.6 (E) Use a dictionary to find words.

Name ______________________________

Practice

Fluency: Phrasing

As I read, I will pay attention to phrasing.

Some say Orville and Wilbur Wright were born to fly.
10 Their 1903 flight was the first of its kind. As children
21 the boys got along well. One night their dad came
31 home early with a present for them. He tossed it up
42 high. Did it just fall and drop? No, instead it sped
53 right by! Why? It had rubber bands to wind up. As the
65 bands unwound, the toy flew. That flying toy might
74 have started a big dream.

79 As grown-ups, the men had a real goal. They wanted
90 to make the first plane and fly it. The men worked
101 hard. Would the plane fly and return to land? Or
111 would it crash? The first test flights didn't go well. But
122 the men weren't unhappy. They still had hope. They
131 found a way to fix the problems.

138 In the winter of 1903, they got their plane to fly. What
150 a sight it was to see a plane flying like a bird! 162

Comprehension Check

1. What started Orville and Wilbur Wright's dream?
2. In what season was the first airplane flight?

	Words Read	–	Number of Errors	=	Words Correct Score
First Read		–		=	
Second Read		–		=	

TEKS 1.3 (I) Monitor accuracy of decoding.
1.5 (A) Read aloud grade-level appropriate text with fluency and comprehension.

Name ______________________________

You can use the Internet to find out about a topic. Put important words, or keywords, in the search box. Then hit GO, and a list of links will pop up.

Write the keywords you might type in the search box to look up the following:

1. You want to know more about the moon. ______________________

2. You want to find out about places to see in New York. ______________________

3. You want to know more about the animal you like best. ______________________

4. You want to find out about a job you would like. ______________________

TEKS 1.14 (D) Use text features to locate specific information in text.
1.24 (B) Use text features in age-appropriate reference works to locate information.

Name ______________________________

Nonfiction gives information about a topic. The information is true.

Listen to the passage. Then complete the items.

Do you like to eat pizza? It's easy to make if you ask an adult for help. First, make the dough. You need flour, yeast, oil, salt, sugar, and warm water. Mix the dough. Then spread it out flat on a pan. Next, pour tomato sauce on top. Then add some cheese on top of the sauce. Last, add peppers, tomatoes, or meat. Some people like cheese pizza because it is yummy. But some people like it with pineapple or even fish on top! What would you like on your pizza?

1. What would be a good title for this story? Circle the best answer.

   Pizza Tastes Good

   How to Make Pizza

2. Work with a partner. Retell what happens first, next, and last when you make a pizza.

3. There are 6 things you need to make the dough. Reread the passage. Write two of the things you need below.

   ______________________ ______________________

TEKS 1.14 (A) Restate the main idea, heard or read.
1.14 (B) Identify important facts or details in text, heard or read.
1.14 (C) Retell the order of events in a text by referring to the words.

Name ______________________________

A **Reading Log** tells about something that you read.

Read a fiction book or a nonfiction book every day this week. Then tell about what you read.

Title ______________________________

Author ______________________________

What I Read About ______________________________

Title ______________________________

Author ______________________________

What I Read About ______________________________

TEKS **1.12** Read independently for a sustained period of time.
1.19 (C) Write brief comments on literary or informational texts.

Name ______________________________

Practice

Phonics: Two Syllable Words: Open and Closed Syllables

A **syllable** is a word part that has one vowel sound. Some words have more than one syllable.

A syllable that ends in a vowel is called an **open syllable**. The vowel sound is usually long.
Examples: **ti**-ger **fro**-zen

A syllable that ends in a consonant is called a **closed syllable**. The vowel sound is usually short.

Examples: **up**-set **vel**-vet

Read each word below. Listen for the two syllables. Write O if the first syllable is an open syllable. Write C if the first syllable is a closed syllable.

1. baby ______
2. pencil ______
3. broken ______
4. zebra ______
5. rabbit ______
6. insect ______

TEKS 1.3 (C) (i) (ii) Use common syllabication patterns to decode words, including closed syllable (CVC) and open syllable (CV).

Name ______________________________

Circle the word that completes each sentence. Then write the word on the line.

1. Where has the cat ______________?
   done gone

2. The girls have ______________ best friends for years.
   been are

3. Let's keep ______________ for the missing dog.
   sending searching

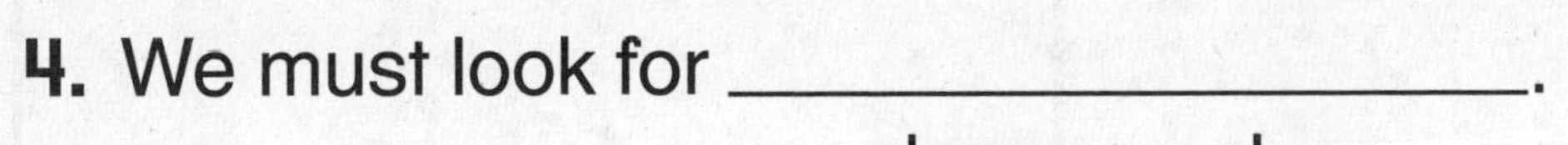

4. We must look for ______________.
   close clues

5. I can't see it. It must be ______________.
   invisible instead

6. "I saw the keys ______________ we left," said Mom.
   other before

TEKS 1.3 (H) Identify and read at least 100 high-frequency words from a commonly used list.

Name ______________________________________

As you read Dot and Jabber and the Big Bug Mystery, fill in the Predictions Chart.

What I Predict	What Happens

How does the information you wrote in this Predictions Chart help you better understand Dot and Jabber and the Big Bug Mystery?

TEKS 1.4 (A) Confirm predictions about what will happen next in text by "reading the part that tells".

Name ____________________

In a **prediction**, you tell what you think will happen next.

Read each story. Then complete the sentence to tell what could happen next.

1. The ship launches. It is flying to the moon. It will

____.

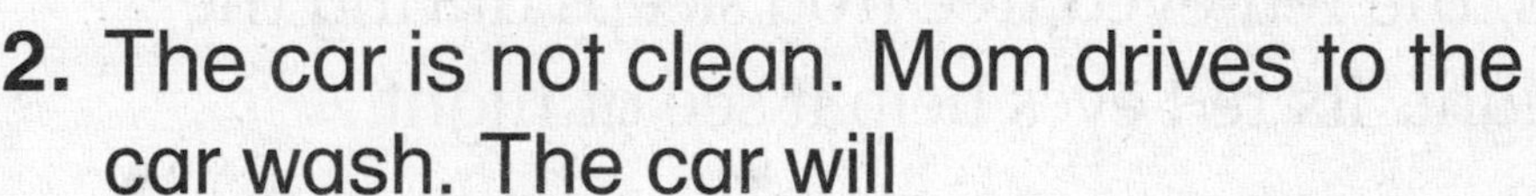

2. The car is not clean. Mom drives to the car wash. The car will

____.

3. It is a windy day. We have kites. We will

____.

4. Dad brings home a bag full of food. He cooks the food. We will

____.

TEKS **1.4 (A)** Confirm predictions about what will happen next in text by "reading the part that tells".

Name ______________________________

If a story is not clear as you read it, ask yourself questions about it. Then **reread** the story. Look for clues to answer your questions.

Read the story. Then answer the questions.

Meet the Red-Eyed Tree Frog

A red-eyed tree frog is different from other frogs. It has red eyes. Its skin is bright green with blue and yellow stripes. Most frogs live in ponds, but the red-eyed tree frog lives in trees. Like other frogs, this frog eats flies and other bugs. Unlike other frogs, the red-eyed tree frog sleeps during the day. It hunts at night. Its red eyes help it see at night.

1. Write a question that you have about red-eyed tree frogs.

____

2. Reread the story. Look for clues to answer your question.

____

____

3. What facts did you learn about red-eyed tree frogs? Draw a circle around that part of the story.

TEKS **1.4 (B)** Ask relevant questions, seek clarification, and locate facts and details about stories and other texts. **1.4 (C)** Monitor comprehension, making corrections when that understanding breaks down. **RC-1 (C)** Monitor and adjust comprehension.

Name ______________________________

Contractions combine two words. The **apostrophe** (') takes the place of any missing letters.

we + will = **we'll** I + am = **I'm** you + have = **you've**

A. Write the contraction or the two words.

1. we + have = ____________

2. he'll = ____________ + ____________

3. I'm = ____________ + ____________

4. she + will = ____________

B. Use the contractions to complete the sentences.

5. ____________ scratching my itch.

6. ____________ be glad when spring is here.

TEKS 1.3 (G) Identify and read contractions.

Name ______________________________

Practice

Vocabulary Strategy: Word Parts: Inflectional Endings *-ed*, *-ing*

An **inflected verb** is a verb with an ending. When you remove the **-ing** or **-ed** ending, you are left with the base word.

inflected verb	**base word**
splash**ing**	splash
splash**ed**	splash

Write the ending. Then write the base word. The first one is done for you.

1. opened ___ed___ ___open___
2. chewing __________ __________
3. pointed __________ __________
4. crawling __________ __________
5. roaring __________ __________
6. talked __________ __________

TEKS 1.3 (E) Read base words with inflectional endings.

Name ________________________________

As I read, I will pay attention to phrasing in the story.

Mark goes to Steph's yard to play.
07 They like the fresh air and have fun building
16 a wooden home. Mark and Steph finish.
23 Steph says, "Now we need to paint the outside."
32 "Let's begin!" Mark says.
36 Steph says, "Let's paint the outside green."
43 Mark begins to laugh. "We can't," he says.
51 "We only have blue and yellow paint."
58 "That's no problem," says Steph. "Watch this."
65 Mark stares while Steph mixes the blue
72 and yellow paint. "It's green!" Mark shouts.
79 "That's correct," says Steph.
83 "Mixing blue and yellow makes green."
89 "I never knew that!" says Mark.
95 We make a good pair! 100

Comprehension Check

1. What are Mark and Steph doing?

2. What do blue and yellow make?

	Words Read	–	Number of Errors	=	Words Correct Score
First Read		–		=	
Second Read		–		=	

TEKS **1.3 (I)** Monitor accuracy of decoding.
1.5 Read aloud grade-level appropriate text with fluency and comprehension.

Practice

Read Aloud: Poetry

Name ______________________________

A **poem** often uses words that start with the same sound or words that rhyme. Poems have interesting words that paint a picture of something in the reader's mind.

Listen to the poem.

I see an insect, and my mind starts to think:
Where does it live? Does it eat or drink?
What color is it? Is it green or blue?
Is its name Tommy, Skip, or Sue?
How many legs, and how many eyes?
How does it move? I wonder if it flies.
Does it run? Does it crawl? Can it swim or jump?
Is it long and thin or rather plump?
All of these things I wonder as I look.
I think I need my science book!

1. Circle the words that rhyme in the poem.
2. Write two more rhyming lines to complete the poem.

____

____

TEKS 1.8 Respond to and use rhyme in poetry.

Name ______________________________

A **head** tells what information is in a section of an article or story.

A. Read the article about spiders.

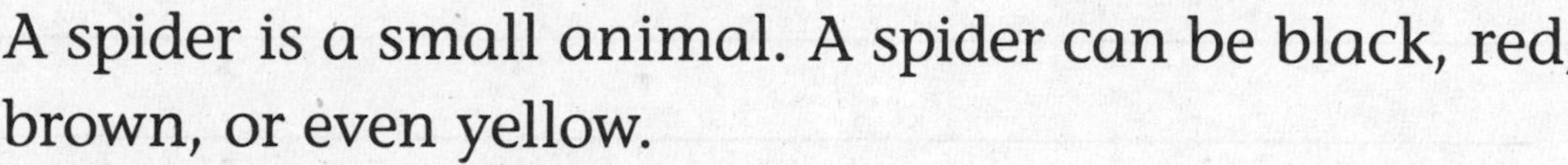

Spiders

A spider is a small animal. A spider can be black, red, brown, or even yellow.

The Body of a Spider

A spider has 2 body parts. It also has 8 legs. An insect has only 6 legs.

The Home of a Spider

A spider lives in a web. It spins a sticky web. When a bug flies into the web, it gets stuck. Then the spider eats it.

B. Answer the questions about the article.

1. Circle the two heads that tell what information is in the sections.
2. Write one fact from each section.

____

____

TEKS 1.14 (D) Use text features to locate specific information in text.

Name ______________________________

A **Reading Log** tells about something that you read.

Read a fiction book or a nonfiction book every day this week. Then tell about what you read.

Title ______________________________

Author ______________________________

What I Read About ______________________________

Title ______________________________

Author ______________________________

What I Read About ______________________________

TEKS 1.12 Read independently for a sustained period of time.
1.19 (C) Write brief comments on literary or informational texts.

Name ______________________________

Some words have more than one **syllable**, or word part.

Read each sentence. Circle the word with two syllables. Write the word on the line.

1. Meg sat at the table with Dad. ______________

2. The turtle has a hard shell. ______________

3. The apple I like best is red. ______________

4. Most clowns know how to juggle. ______________

5. The horse is in the stable. ______________

TEKS **1.3 (C) (iii)** Use common syllabication patterns to decode words, including final stable syllable.

Name ______________________________

straight	certain	begin	brought
minutes	around	daydream	cancel

Choose the correct word from the box and write it on the line.

1. Ann had a ________________.

2. How did the dream ________________?

3. A cat ________________ Ann a beautiful car.

4. Ann drove the car ________________ town.

5. Then she went ________________ back home.

TEKS 1.3 (H) Identify and read at least 100 high-frequency words from a commonly used list.

Name ______________________________

Practice

Comprehension: Character and Setting Chart

As you read Super Oscar, fill in the Character and Setting Chart.

Character	Setting

How does the information you wrote in this Character and Setting Chart help you retell Super Oscar?

TEKS **1.9 (B)** Describe characters in a story and the reasons for their actions and feelings.

Name ______________________

The **characters** are the people or animals in a story.

The **setting** is where the story happens.

Look at the pictures. Answer the questions about the characters and setting.

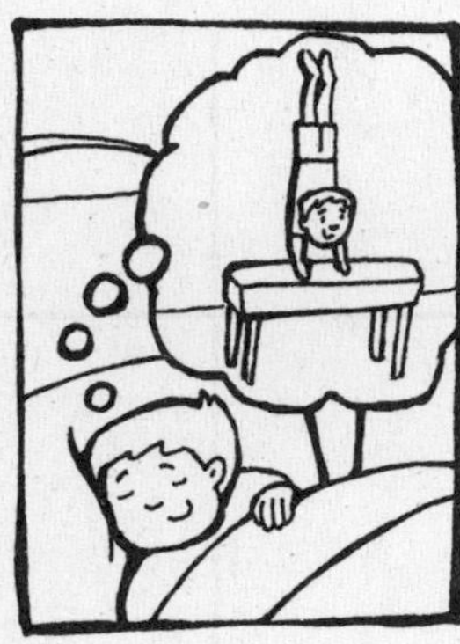

1. Who is the story about? ______________________

2. Where does the story happen? ______________________

3. How does the character feel at the end?

____

TEKS 1.9 (B) Describe characters in a story and the reason for their actions and feelings.

Name ______________________________

If a story is not clear as you read it, ask yourself questions about it. Then **reread** the story. Look for clues to answer your questions.

Read the story. Then answer the questions.

A Rainy Day in August

It's raining out, but it will still be fun because I am going to a movie downtown! I have not been to a movie in a long time. I am very excited. Dad pays for our tickets, and we go inside. Mom gives me money to get nachos with cheese sauce. Then it's time to find a good seat. Soon, the movie starts. It is so silly that it causes us to laugh out loud. I'm so glad that we can enjoy this rainy day in August together.

1. Write a question that you have about this special day.

____

2. Reread the story. Look for clues to answer your question.

____

____

Name ______________________

A **compound word** is made up of smaller words.

pop + corn = **popcorn**

pea + nuts = **peanuts**

Compound words have more than one syllable.

A. Match a word on the left to a word on the right to make a compound word. Then write the word.

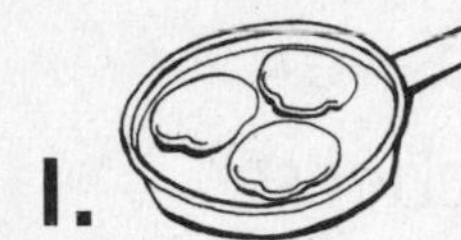

1. pan end ______________________

2. camp dream ______________________

3. day cakes ______________________

4. week ground ______________________

B. Use one compound word in a sentence.

5. ______________________

TEKS 1.3 (F) Use knowledge of the meaning of base words to identify and read common compound words. 1.6 (B) Determine the meaning of compound words using knowledge of the meaning of their individual component words.

Name ______________________________

Use the underlined context clues to figure out the meaning of the word in bold letters. Then match the word to its meaning. Write the correct letter on the line.

a. moved round and round **b.** came back

c. tapped gently **d.** to keep safe

e. a bridge that can be raised and lowered

1. The royal family **returned** home from a trip to the countryside. ____

2. The king, queen, and prince crossed over the **drawbridge** toward the castle. ____

3. The happy queen kissed the prince and **patted** him on the head. ____

4. Water from the river **swirled** in the moat. ____

5. The moat and the drawbridge **protect** the castle from strangers. ____

TEKS **1.6 (C)** Determine what words mean from how they are used in a sentence, either heard or read.

Name ________________________________

As I read, I will pay attention to phrasing in the story.

Betty was very happy. Today was her birthday.
08 She had been planning a little party all week.
17 She had many games for her friends to play.
26 Many children came to the party.
32 "Let's play Pin the Tail on the Kitten," Betty said.
42 "I just need to get the blindfold."
49 Betty looked for the blindfold.
54 She wasn't able to find it.
60 "I don't know where it's gone," she said.
68 The children began searching, too.
73 They looked behind the couch. They looked under the rug.
83 The blindfold was missing. Then the cat came in.
92 "Look!" shouted Betty. "Kitty has it!
98 She wants to play Pin the Tail on the Kitten, too!" 109

Comprehension Check

1. What game are they trying to play?

2. Who stole the blindfold?

	Words Read	–	Number of Errors	=	Words Correct Score
First Read		–		=	
Second Read		–		=	

TEKS 1.3 (I) Monitor accuracy of decoding.
1.5 Read aloud grade-level appropriate text with fluency and comprehension.

Name ______________________________

A **fairy tale** is a story that has make-believe and magical events.

Listen to the story. Then answer the questions.

Once upon a time, there was a girl named Rapunzel. A mean woman trapped Rapunzel and locked her in a tall tower. The woman cast a spell on the tower so that it had no door. Over time, Rapunzel's hair grew and grew. When the woman came to visit, she would call, "Rapunzel, Rapunzel, let down your hair!" Rapunzel would let her long hair fall down. The woman would climb it like a rope. One day, a prince rode by. He saw Rapunzel, and he fell in love. The woman came to visit. The prince hid and watched how the woman got in and out of the tower. When the woman left, he came out and said, "Rapunzel, Rapunzel, let down your hair!" Rapunzel let her hair down to the prince. The prince climbed up Rapunzel's hair and saved her. And they lived happily ever after.

1. Circle the words that let you know this is a fairy tale.
2. What does the phrase "Once upon a time" mean?

____

____

TEKS 1.7 (B) Explain the function of recurring phrases in traditional folk and fairy tales.

Name ________________________________

Practice

Literary Element: Rhyming Pattern

Some poems have a **rhyming pattern**.

In some poems, the second line of a verse rhymes with the fourth line.

A. Circle the two rhyming words in each poem.

The sun is out.
What a fine day!
Will you come out with me
And play?

I saw a seed
Fall to the ground.
It never made
A sound.

You want to play ball,
But what I'd like
Is to ride round and round
On my brand new bike.

I look up at
The sky at night,
And watch the stars
That shine so bright.

B. Think of more rhyming pairs. Write the pairs below.

1. ________________ ________________

2. ________________ ________________

Name ______________________________

A **Reading Log** tells about something that you read.

Read a fiction book or a nonfiction book every day this week. Then tell about what you read.

Title ______________________________

Author ______________________________

What I Read About ______________________________

____

Title ______________________________

Author ______________________________

What I Read About ______________________________

____

TEKS **1.12** Read independently for a sustained period of time.
1.19 (C) Write brief comments on literary or informational texts.

Contents

Show What You Know

Unit 1

Unit 2

Unit 3

Unit 4

Unit 5

Unit 6

Additional Practice

Student Name ______________________

DIRECTIONS
Answer these questions about "Jill and Nat" (pp. 132–133).

1 What does Jill do first?

(A) Plays with Nat

(B) Rides up the hill

(C) Digs in the sand

2 What does Jill do then?

(A) Jumps up

(B) Plays with Nat

(C) Runs down

3 How old is Nat?

(A) Five

(B) Six

(C) Ten

Student Name ______________________________

4 What does Nat do first?

(A) Rides up the hill

(B) Picks a pet

(C) Digs in the sand

5 What does Nat do then?

(A) Runs up the hill

(B) Digs with Jill

(C) Rides down

STOP

Student Name____

DIRECTIONS
Answer these questions about "Cats and Dogs" (pp. 134–135).

1 Look at the picture of a cat. The cat —

(A) jumps

(B) rests

(C) digs

2 Look at the picture of a cat. What does a cat have by its nose?

(A) Whiskers

(B) Paws

(C) Tail

3 Look at the picture of a dog. The dog —

(A) digs in the sand

(B) moves its ears

(C) looks up

GO ON

Student Name____

4 Look at the picture of a dog. The dog has —

Ⓐ a tail

Ⓑ a tree

Ⓒ whiskers

5 What part is named in both pictures?

Ⓐ Nose

Ⓑ Ear

Ⓒ Paw

STOP

Student Name ____________________

DIRECTIONS
Answer these questions about "Frog Lost" (pp. 142–143).

1 What is the problem in the story?

(A) Meg will not help Gus.

(B) Gus is sick.

(C) Frog is lost.

2 Where does Gus look first?

(A) In his pack

(B) Under the bed

(C) In the sink

3 Where does Meg look next?

(A) In her pack

(B) On a dish

(C) In a pond

Student Name ______________________________

4 How does Meg solve the problem?

(A) She looks under the bed.

(B) She yells to Frog.

(C) She asks, "What does Frog like to do?"

5 What happens in this story?

(A) Gus and Meg want Frog.
Frog hops under the bed.

(B) Meg and Gus look for Frog.
Frog is in the sink.

(C) Gus is lost.
Megs looks for Gus.

STOP

Student Name________________________________

DIRECTIONS
Answer these questions about "Make a Book!" (pp. 144–145).

1 The diagram on page 144 shows the parts of a —

(A) house

(B) door

(C) book

2 The name of the book is on the —

(A) front cover

(B) inside pages

(C) back cover

3 What do you do with the paper to make a book?

(A) Rip it

(B) Cut it

(C) Fold it

Student Name ______________________________

4 What should you draw on the cover?

(A) A door

(B) A pet

(C) A man

5 What should you do last with your book?

(A) Write about your pictures

(B) Show it to a friend

(C) Draw three things

STOP

Student Name____

DIRECTIONS
Answer these questions about "Kate and June" (pp. 148–149).

1 Which part of the story shows you where Kate and June will go?

(A) **Kate:** Can you play with me, June?

(B) **June:** OK. But I don't have much time.

(C) **Kate:** I'd like to swing in the park.

2 Which part shows you that June has something else she needs to do?

(A) **Kate:** Can you play with me, June?

(B) **June:** OK. But I don't have much time.

(C) **Kate:** I'd like to swing in the park.

3 What will Kate do in the park?

(A) Swing

(B) Jump

(C) Draw

Student Name ____________________

4 Which part shows you how Kate and June will get to the park?

(A) **Kate:** I'd like to swing in the park.

(B) **Kate:** What do you want to do?

(C) **June:** I want to ride bikes.

5 How will Kate and June get to the park next time?

(A) Hop

(B) Ride

(C) Run

STOP

Student Name ____________________

DIRECTIONS
Answer these questions about "Made at Home" (pp. 150–151).

1 What is the main idea of this article?

(A) Long ago, kids made toys.

(B) Today kids shop for toys and games.

(C) Long ago, kids did not play ball.

2 What is the last part of the article mostly about?

(A) Jobs

(B) Kites

(C) Stick ball

3 What did kids use to make kites?

(A) Bags

(B) Cloth

(C) Corn husks

Student Name ______________________________

4 Look at the doll on page 151. What is it made of?

(A) Rags

(B) Sticks

(C) Corn husks

5 In the picture on page 151, the girl wears —

(A) a hat

(B) a dress

(C) some pants

STOP

Student Name ____________________

DIRECTIONS
Answer these questions about "Ray and His Bones" (pp. 138–139).

1 Ray buried his bones in the —

(A) spring

(B) summer

(C) winter

2 Ray was thrilled. The word <u>thrilled</u> means —

(A) happy

(B) pretty

(C) big

3 What does Ray love?

(A) Snow

(B) Bones

(C) Friends

Student Name ______________________________

4 Where did Ray bury the bones?

(A) At friends' homes

(B) In the backyard

(C) By the school

5 What happened after the winter? Support your answer with details from the story.

____

____

____

____

STOP

Student Name ______________________________

DIRECTIONS
Answer these questions about "As Tall as the Trees." (pp. 140–141)

1 Look at this web.

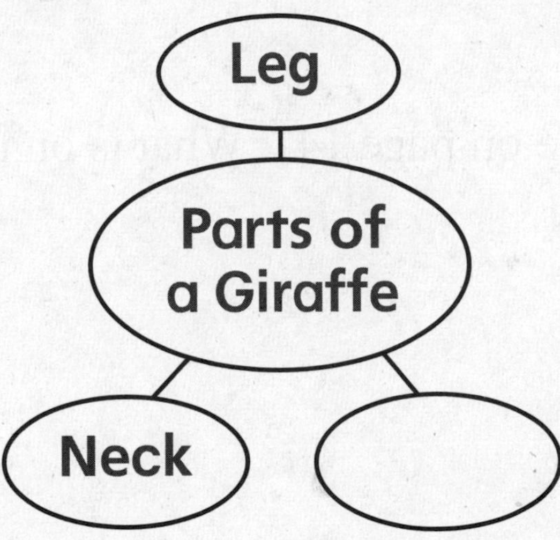

Which word belongs in the empty circle?

(A) Tall

(B) Leaves

(C) Mane

2 Look at the picture on page 140. Giraffes get food and water from —

(A) cows

(B) leaves

(C) people

Student Name ______________________

3 Giraffes are the tallest mammals. What does mammal mean?

(A) Bull

(B) Tree

(C) Animal

4 Look at the picture on page 141. What is on the giraffe's head?

(A) Calf

(B) Neck

(C) Horn

5 Tell how tall a male giraffe is when it is born and how tall it grows. Support your answer with details from the story.

____

____

____

____

STOP

Student Name______________________________

DIRECTIONS

Answer these questions about "What Grasshopper Learned" (pp. 160–161).

1 Use the chart to answer the question.

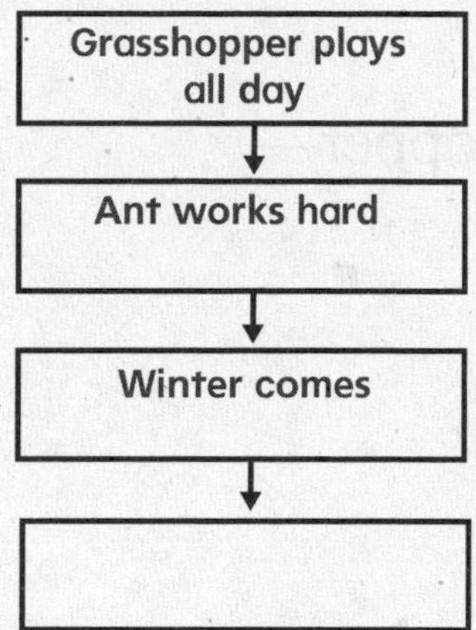

Which event belongs in the empty box?

(A) Grasshopper plays music.

(B) Grasshopper has no food.

(C) Ant runs out of food.

2 What is a <u>grasshopper</u>?

(A) An animal that swims in a pond

(B) An animal that plays in the snow

(C) An animal that hops in the grass

Student Name ______________________________

3 What is a <u>snowstorm</u>?

(A) A storm with snow

(B) A day of storms

(C) A man made of snow

4 While Ant works, Grasshopper—

(A) makes his home

(B) plays music

(C) asks for corn

5 How are Ant and Grasshopper different? Explain your answer and support it with details from the story.

____

____

____

____

STOP

Student Name________________________________

DIRECTIONS
Answer these questions about "What Does the Weather Chart Say?" (pp. 162–163).

1 How can you tell which words are important in paragraph 1?

(A) They are in bold print.

(B) They are in capital letters.

(C) They are in the article.

2 Weather may be hot, warm, or —

(A) chart

(B) day

(C) cold

3 Look at the chart on page 163. What was the weather like on Wednesday?

(A) There were clouds.

(B) There was snow.

(C) There was wind.

Student Name ____________________

4 Look at the chart on page 163. People needed umbrellas on —

(A) Monday

(B) Tuesday

(C) Friday

5 How was the weather different on Tuesday and Thursday? Explain your answer and support it with details from the article.

____

____

____

____

STOP

Student Name________________________________

DIRECTIONS
Answer these questions about "The Picnic Tent" (pp. 168–169).

1 Look at the diagram about the story.

Setting	What the Characters Do There
Under the table	

What belongs in the empty box?

(A) Eat lunch and do mazes

(B) Fly their kites

(C) Play catch

2 Jen and James go to a —

(A) park

(B) school

(C) camp

Student Name ____________________

3 When the rain begins, James wants to —

(A) go home

(B) keep playing

(C) ride his bike

4 Jen removed the plastic cloth from the table. What does <u>removed</u> mean?

(A) Climbed over

(B) Sat on

(C) Took off

5 What will Jen and James probably do next? Explain your answer and support it with details from the story.

____

____

____

____

STOP

Student Name________________________________

DIRECTIONS
Answer these questions about "Life of a Butterfly" (pp. 170–171) .

1 When the egg hatches, a caterpillar crawls out. What does hatches mean?

(A) Falls

(B) Cooks

(C) Opens

2 Look at the caption on page 170. How long do most butterflies live?

(A) One or two days

(B) One to two weeks

(C) One to two years

3 Look at the chart on page 171. What is step 3 in a butterfly's life?

(A) Pupa

(B) Egg

(C) Butterfly

Student Name ______________________________

4 Look at the chart on page 171. When in a butterfly's life is it a caterpillar?

Ⓐ Step 1

Ⓑ Step 2

Ⓒ Step 3

5 What will a butterfly do after its wings dry? Explain your answer and support it with details from the article.

____

____

____

____

STOP

Name ______________________________

The **short i** vowel sound is spelled with the letter **i**.

pig fin

The **short a** vowel sound is spelled with the letter **a**.

back cat

Read the words below. Write a rhyming word for each word. Then use two of the words in a sentence.

1. fix ______________________

2. sit ______________________

3. pan ______________________

4. lap ______________________

____

____

TEKS **1.3 (A) (2) (ii) (3)** Decode words in isolation by applying common letter-sound correspondences, including single letters (vowels) including short i.

Name ______________________________

The **short i** vowel sound is spelled with the letter **i**.

p**i**g f**i**n

The **short a** vowel sound is spelled with the letter **a**.

b**a**ck c**a**t

Read the words. Cut out the words. Sort the words by vowel sound.

lick	tag	hip	sat
fill	map	had	quit

TEKS 1.3 (A) (2) (ii) (3) Decode words in isolation by applying common letter-sound correspondences, including single letters (vowels) including short i.

Name ______________________________

The **short i** vowel sound is spelled with the letter **i**.

pig fin

The **short a** vowel sound is spelled with the letter **a**.

back cat

Read the words below. Then reread <u>Jim Had a Big Hit!</u> Add words from the story to each list.

pig	cat

TEKS **1.3 (A) (2) (ii) (3)** Decode words in isolation by applying common letter-sound correspondences, including single letters (vowels) including short i.

Name ______________________________

The **short o** vowel sound is spelled with the letter **o**.

l**o**g b**o**x

Two letters can form an **end blend**. Listen for each consonant sound.

ha**nd** pa**st**

Two letters can form a **beginning blend**. Listen for each consonant sound.

black **cl**ip

Read the words. Cut out the words. Sort the words by spelling pattern.

Short o	End blend	Beginning blend

mom	sink	slick	list
land	got	task	glad
clam	flat	pond	sock

TEKS 1.3 (A) (2) (i) (ii) (iii) Decode words in isolation by applying common letter-sound correspondences, including single letters (consonants and vowels) and consonant blends.

Name ______________________________

The **short e** vowel sound is spelled with the letter **e**.

le**g** he**n**

The **short o** vowel sound is spelled with the letter **o**.

lo**g** bo**x**

Two letters can form a **blend**. Listen for each consonant sound in the final **blend**.

ha**nd** pa**st**

Read the words. Cut out the words. Sort the words by spelling pattern.

Short e	Short o	Blend

let	ask	test	hop
plant	help	blot	went
wind	gift	box	mop

TEKS **1.3 (A) (2) (i) (ii) (iii)** Decode words in isolation by applying common letter-sound correspondences, including single letters (consonants and vowels) and consonant blends.

Name ______________________________

Two letters can form a **blend**. Listen for each consonant sound in the consonant **blend**.

crab **sn**ap

The **short e** vowel sound is spelled with the letter **e**.

l**e**g h**e**n

The **short o** vowel sound is spelled with the letter **o**.

l**o**g b**o**x

Read the words. Cut out the words. Sort the words by spelling pattern.

Consonant blends	Short e	Short o

lot	swam	left	spend
track	mop	rock	hot
stem	nest	stick	grab

TEKS 1.3 (A) (2) (i) (ii) (iii) Decode words in isolation by applying common letter-sound correspondences, including single letters (consonants and vowels) and consonant blends.

Name ______________________________

The **short u** vowel sound is spelled with the letter **u.**

b**u**n p**u**p t**u**b

Two letters can form a **blend**. Listen to the sounds that **cr**, **sn**, and **st** stand for.

crab **sn**ap **st**ep

The **short e** vowel sound is spelled with the letter **e.**

l**e**g h**e**n p**e**n

Read the words. Cut out the words. Sort the words by spelling pattern.

Short u	Consonant blend	Short e

sun	trick	yes	grass
ten	mud	spot	get
stamp	puff	must	best

TEKS 1.3 (A) (2) (i) (ii) (iii) Decode words in isolation by applying common letter-sound correspondences, including single letters (consonants and vowels) and consonant blends.

Name ______________________________

Two letters can form a **digraph**. Listen to the sounds that **sh**, **th**, and **ng** stand for.

think **sh**ip swi**ng**

The **short u** vowel sound is spelled with the letter **u**.

b**u**n p**u**p t**u**b

Two letters can form a **blend**. Listen to the sounds that **cr**, **sn**, and **gr** stand for.

crab **sn**ap **gr**ab

Read the words. Cut out the words. Sort the words by vowel spelling pattern.

Digraphs	Short u	Blends

thump	sing	snip	spell
plug	bus	shack	grass
trip	just	crash	fun

TEKS 1.3 (A) (2) (i) (ii) (iii) (iv) Decode words in isolation by applying common letter-sound correspondences, including single letters (consonants and vowels), consonant blends and consonant digraphs.

Name ______________________

Practice

Phonics: Decoding

The letter **j** stands for the sound at the beginning of **j**et.

The letters **qu** together stand for the sound at the beginning of **qu**ilt.

Read each word. Write two more words with the underlined sound-spelling pattern.

job	______	______
just	______	______
quit	______	______
quack	______	______

TEKS **1.3 (A) (2) (i) (9) (15)** Decode words in isolation by applying common letter-sound correspondences, including single letters (consonants) including j and qu=/kw/.

Name ______________________________

The letter **j** stands for the sound at the beginning of **j**et.

The letters **qu** together stand for the sound at the beginning of **qu**ilt.

Read the words. Cut out the words. Sort the words by the beginning sound.

	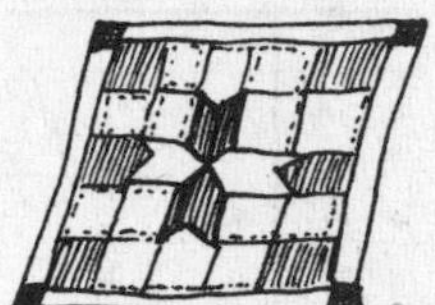

quick	jog	jam	quit
jump	quiz	jazz	quack

TEKS 1.3 (A) (2) (i) (9) (15) Decode words in isolation by applying common letter-sound correspondences, including single letters (consonants) including j and qu=/kw/.

Name ______________________________

The letter **s** can sometimes stand for the sound at the end of ha**s**.
The letter **x** stands for the sounds at the end of si**x**.

Read each word. Write one more word with the underlined sound-spelling pattern.

has	
is	
mix	
wax	

TEKS 1.3 (A) (2) (i) (18) (22) Decode words in isolation by applying common letter-sound correspondences, including single letters (consonants) including s=/z/ and x=/ks/.

Name ______________________________

The letter **s** can sometimes stand for the sound at the end of ha**s**.

The letter **x** stands for the sounds at the end of si**x**.

Read the words below. Write a rhyming word for each word. Then use two of the words in a sentence.

1. as ______________________

2. his ______________________

3. mix ______________________

4. fox ______________________

____

____

TEKS 1.3 (A) (2) (i) (18) (22) Decode words in isolation by applying common letter-sound correspondences, including single letters (consonants) including s=/z/ and x=/ks/.

Name ______________________________

The letter **y** stands for the sound at the beginning of **y**es and **y**ak.

The letter **z** stands for the sound at the beginning of **z**ip and at the end of fi**zz**.

Read each word. Write two more words with the underlined sound-spelling pattern.

yam	________	________
yell	________	________
zip	________	________
jazz	________	________

TEKS 1.3 (A) (2) (i) (23) (24) Decode words in isolation by applying common letter-sound correspondences, including single letters (consonants) including y and z.

Name ______________________________

The letter **y** stands for the sound at the beginning of **y**es and **y**ak.

The letter **z** stands for the sound at the beginning of **z**ip and at the end of fi**zz**.

Read the words. Cut out the words. Sort the words by the consonant sound.

yet	zig-zag	yam	quiz
yell	zip	fuzz	yak

TEKS 1.3 (A) (2) (i) (23) (24) Decode words in isolation by applying common letter-sound correspondences, including single letters (consonants) y and z.

Name ______________________________

Two letters can form a consonant digraph. Listen to the sounds that the consonant digraphs **sh** and **th** stand for.

ship fi**sh** **th**ink pa**th**

Read the words below. Then reread <u>This and That</u>. Add words from the story to each list.

fi**sh**	**th**ing

TEKS 1.3 (A) (2) (iv) (3) (4) Decode words in isolation by applying common letter-sound correspondences, including consonant digraphs including sh and th=as in thing.

Name ______________________

Practice

Phonics: Decoding

Two letters can form a consonant digraph. Listen to the sounds that the consonant digraphs **sh** and **th** stand for.

ship fi**sh** **th**ink pa**th**

Read each word. Write two more words with the underlined sound-spelling pattern.

<u>sh</u>ock	______	______
sma<u>sh</u>	______	______
<u>th</u>ank	______	______
ba<u>th</u>	______	______

TEKS 1.3 (A) (2) (iv) (3) (4) Decode words in isolation by applying common letter-suond correspondence, including consonant digraphs including sh and th=as in thing.

Name ______________________________

Two letters can form a consonant digraph. The consonant digraph **ck** stands for the ending sound in so**ck**.

The consonant digraph **ng** stands for the ending sound in swi**ng**.

Read the words below. Write a rhyming word for each word. Then use two of the words in a sentence.

1. block ______________________________

2. quack ______________________________

3. spring ______________________________

4. clang ______________________________

____

____

TEKS **1.3 (A) (2) (iv) (6) (7)** Decode words in isolation by applying common letter-sound correspondences, including consonant digraphs including ng and ck.

Name ___________________________

Practice

Phonics: Decoding

Two letters can form a consonant digraph. The consonant digraph **ck** stands for the ending sound in so**ck**.

The consonant digraph **ng** stands for the ending sound in swi**ng**.

Read the words. Cut out the words. Sort the words by the ending sound.

back	king	hang	neck
sang	block	string	pick

TEKS 1.3 (A) (2) (iv) (6) (7) Decode words in isolation by applying common letter-sound correspondences, including consonant digraphs including ng and ck.

Name ____________________

The **long a** vowel sound is spelled with the letters **a_e**.

g**ate** t**ape**

Two letters can form a **digraph**. Listen to the sounds that **sh**, **th**, and **ng** stand for.

think **sh**ip swi**ng**

The letter **u** stands for the middle sound in b**u**s.

b**u**n p**u**p t**u**b

Read the words. Cut out the words. Sort the words by spelling pattern.

Long a	Digraphs	Short u

late	with	came	hut
thank	hang	gate	sun
plugs	name	fun	crash

TEKS 1.3 (A) (2) (i) (ii) (iii) (iv) Decode words in isolation by applying common letter-sound correspondences, including single letters (consonants and vowels), consonant blends, and consonant digraphs.

Name ____________________

The **long i** vowel sound is spelled with the letters **i_e**.

h**i**k**e** f**i**v**e**

The **long a** vowel sound is spelled with the letters **a_e**.

g**a**t**e** t**a**p**e**

Two letters can form a **digraph**. Listen to the sounds that **sh**, **th**, and **ng** stand for. The digraph **dge** has three letters.

think **sh**ip swi**ng** e**dge**

Read the words. Cut out the words. Sort the words by spelling pattern.

Long i	Long a	Digraphs

fine	safe	with	lake
snake	crush	time	them
thing	smile	page	badge

TEKS 1.3 (A) (2) (i) (ii) (iii) (iv) Decode words in isolation by applying common letter-sound correspondences, including single letters (consonants and vowels), consonant blends, and consonant digraphs.

Name ______________________________

Practice

Phonics: Decoding

The letters **tch** and the letters **ch** stand for the sound in ma**tch**, **ch**op, and crun**ch**.

Read the words below. Write a rhyming word for each word. Then use two of the words in a sentence.

1. crunch ______________________

2. such ______________________

3. match ______________________

4. stitch ______________________

____

____

TEKS **1.3 (A) (2) (iv) (2)** Decode words in isolation by applying common letter-sound correspondences, including consonant digraphs including tch.

Name ______________________________

The letters **ch**, **tch**, **wh**, **ph**, **dge** can form **consonant digraphs.**

chin   di**tch**   **wh**en   gra**ph**   e**dge**

The **long i** vowel sound is spelled with the letters **i_e**.

h**i**k**e**   f**i**v**e**

The **long a** vowel sound is spelled with the letters **a_e**.

g**a**t**e**   t**a**p**e**

Read the words. Cut out the words. Sort the words by spelling pattern.

Digraphs	Long i	Long a

cage	stitch	came	graph
dive	like	check	shape
which	hedge	lime	wide

TEKS **1.3 (A) (2) (i) (ii) (iv)** Decode words in isolation by applying common letter-sound correspondences, including single letters (consonants and vowels) and consonant digraphs.

Name ______________________________

The letters **tch** and the letters **ch** stand for the sound in ma**tch**, **ch**op, and crun**ch**.

Read the words below. Then reread <u>Such a Grand Day!</u> Add words from the story to each list.

ma**tch**	**ch**op	crun**ch**

TEKS 1.3 (A) (2) (iv) (2) Decode words in isolation by applying common letter-sound correspondences, including consonant digraphs including tch.

Name ____________________

The **long a** vowel sound can be spelled with the letters **a_e** as in g**ate** and t**ape**.

The **long o** vowel sound can be spelled with the letters **o_e** as in b**one** and r**ope**.

Read the words below. Write a rhyming word for each word.

1. cane ____________________

2. stole ____________________

3. blame ____________________

4. broke ____________________

5. flake ____________________

6. hope ____________________

TEKS **1.3 (A) (2) (ii) (6) (9)** Decode words in isolation by applying common letter-sound correspondences, including single letters (vowels) including long a (a-e) and long o (o-e).

Name ______________________________

The **long a** vowel sound can be spelled with the letters **a_e** as in g**a**t**e** and t**a**p**e**.

The **long o** vowel sound can be spelled with the letters **o_e** as in b**o**n**e** and r**o**p**e**.

Read each word. Write two more words with the underlined sound-spelling pattern.

stale	____________	____________
rose	____________	____________
tame	____________	____________
mope	____________	____________

TEKS 1.3 (A) (2) (ii) (6) (9) Decode words in isolation by applying common letter-sound correspondences, including single letters (vowels) including long a (a-e) and long o (o-e).

Name ______________________________

The **long a** vowel sound can be spelled with the letters **a_e** as in g**a**t**e** and t**a**p**e**.

The **long o** vowel sound can be spelled with the letters **o_e** as in b**o**n**e** and r**o**p**e**.

Read the words. Cut out the words. Sort the words by vowel spelling pattern.

skate	lane	hope	pole
game	stove	lake	broke

TEKS 1.3 (A) (2) (ii) (6) (9) Decode words in isolation by applying common letter-sound correspondences, including single letters (vowels) including long a (a-e) and long o (o-e).

Name ______________________________

The **long a** vowel sound can be spelled with the letters **a_e** as in g**ate** and t**ape**.

The **long o** vowel sound can be spelled with the letters **o_e** as in b**one** and r**ope**.

Read the words below. Then reread Mole Bakes at Home. Add words from the story to each list.

gate	bone

TEKS **1.3 (A) (2) (ii) (6) (9)** Decode words in isolation by applying common letter-sound correspondences, including single letters (vowels) including long a (a-e) and long o (o-e).

Name ______________________________

The letters **–dge** and the letters **–ge** stand for the sound at the end of **bridge** and **age**.

bri**dge** a**ge**

Read the words below. Write a rhyming word for each word. Then use two of the words in a sentence.

1. age ______________________________

2. budge ______________________________

3. ledge ______________________________

4. page ______________________________

____

____

TEKS 1.3 (A) (2) (iv) (9) Decode words in isolation by applying common letter-sound correspondences, including consonant digraphs including -dge.

Name ____________________

The letters –**dge** and the letters –**ge** stand for the sound at the end of **bridge** and **age**.

bri**dge** a**ge**

Read each word. Write two more words with the underlined sound-spelling pattern.

age	____________	____________
huge	____________	____________
ridge	____________	____________
badge	____________	____________

TEKS 1.3 (A) (2) (iv) (9) Decode words in isolation by applying common letter-sound correspondences, including consonant digraphs including -dge.

Name ______________________________

The letters –**dge** and the letters –**ge** stand for the sound at the end of **bridge** and **age**.

bri**dge** a**ge**

Read the words. Cut out the words. Sort the words by the ending spelling pattern.

page	ledge	huge	badge
stage	dodge	smudge	wage

TEKS 1.3 (A) (2) (iv) (9) Decode words in isolation by applying common letter-sound correspondences, including consonant digraphs including -dge.

Name ____________________

The **long a** vowel sound can be spelled **ai** and **ay**.

s**ai**l h**ay**

Read the words below. Write a rhyming word for each word. Then use two of the words in a sentence.

1. gray ____________________

2. maid ____________________

3. brain ____________________

4. sway ____________________

TEKS 1.3 (A) (2) (v) (9) (10) Decode words in isolation by applying common letter-sound correspondences, including vowel digraphs including ay and ai.

Name ______________________________

The **long a** vowel sound can be spelled **ai** and **ay**.

s**ai**l h**ay**

Read the words. Cut out the words. Sort the words by vowel spelling pattern.

stay	clay	pail	wait
frail	way	main	play

TEKS **1.3 (A) (2) (v) (9) (10)** Decode words in isolation by applying common letter-sound correspondences, including vowel digraphs including ay and ai.

Name ______________________________

The **long a** vowel sound can be spelled **ai** and **ay**.

s**ai**l h**ay**

Read each word. Write two more words with the underlined sound-spelling pattern.

day	________	________
snail	________	________
spray	________	________
drain	________	________

TEKS 1.3 (A) (2) (v) (9) (10) Decode words in isolation by applying common letter-sound correspondences, including vowel digraphs including ay and ai.

Name ______________________________

The **long e** vowel sound can be spelled with the letters **e**, **ee**, and **ie**.

m**e** t**ee**th p**ie**ce

Read each word. Write two more words with the underlined sound-spelling pattern.

be	____________	____________
tree	____________	____________
field	____________	____________

TEKS 1.3 (A) (2) (ii) (7); (v) (5) (15) Decode words in isolation by applying common letter-sound correspondences, including single letters (vowels) including long e (e) and including vowel digraphs including ee and ie as in chief.

Name ______________________________

The **long e** vowel sound can be spelled with the letters **e**, **ee**, and **ie**.

m**e** tr**ee** pi**e**ce

Read the words below. Write a rhyming word for each word.

1. we ______________________________

2. free ______________________________

3. brief ______________________________

4. she ______________________________

5. shield ______________________________

6. sheep ______________________________

TEKS **1.3 (A) (2) (ii) (7); (v) (5) (15)** Decode words in isolation by applying common letter-sound correspondences, including single letters (vowels) including long e (e) and including vowel digraphs including ee and ie as in chief.

Practice

Phonics: Decoding

Name ______________________________

The **long e** vowel sound can be spelled with the letters **e**, **ee**, and **ie**.

m**e** t**ee**th p**ie**ce

Read the words. Cut out the words. Sort the words by vowel spelling pattern.

m**e**	t**ee**th	p**ie**ce

he	flee	niece	chief
spree	we	field	she
be	thief	bee	three

TEKS 1.3 (A) (2) (ii) (7); (v) (5) (15) Decode words in isolation by applying common letter-sound correspondences, including single letters (vowels) including long e (e) and including vowel digraphs including ee and ie as in chief.

Name ______________________________

The **long e** vowel sound can be spelled with the letters **e**, **ee**, and **ie**.

m**e** t**ee**th p**ie**ce

Read the words below. Then reread Fox and the Green Grapes. Add words from the story to each list.

m**e**	t**ee**th	p**ie**ce

TEKS 1.3 (A) (2) (ii) (7); (v) (5) (15) Decode words in isolation by applying common letter-sound correspondences, including single letters (vowels) including long e (e) and including vowel digraphs including ee and ie as in chief.

Name ______________________________

The **long o** vowel sound is spelled with the letters **o**, **oa**, **ow**, and **oe**.

c**o**ld c**oa**t sn**ow** d**oe**

The **long e** vowel sound is spelled with the letters **e**, **ee**, **ea**, and **ie**.

m**e** t**ee**th s**ea**l p**ie**ce

The **long a** vowel sound is spelled **ai** and **ay**.

s**ai**l cl**ay**

Read the words. Cut out the words. Sort the words by spelling pattern.

Long o	Long e	Long a

no	read	tree	field
be	stay	main	toe
train	goat	throw	gray

TEKS 1.3 (A) (2) (i) (ii) (v) Decode words in isolation by applying common letter-sound correspondences, including single letters (consonants and vowels) and vowel digraphs.

Name ____________________________________

The **long o** vowel sound can be spelled with the letters **o**, **oa**, and **ow**.

c**o**ld   c**oa**t   sn**ow**

Read each word. Write two more words with the underlined sound-spelling pattern.

gold	______	______
throw	______	______
float	______	______

TEKS 1.3 (A) (2) (v) (7) Decode words in isolation by applying common letter-sound correspondences, including vowel digraphs including ow as in snow.

Name ____________________

The **long o** vowel sound can be spelled with the letters **o**, **oa**, and **ow**.

c**o**ld   c**oa**t   sn**ow**

Read the words below. Write a rhyming word for each word.

1. no ____________________

2. loan ____________________

3. blown ____________________

4. boast ____________________

5. sold ____________________

6. grow ____________________

TEKS 1.3 (A) (2) (v) (7) Decode words in isolation by applying common letter-sound correspondences, including vowel digraphs including ow as in snow.

Name ______________________________

The **long o** vowel sound can be spelled with the letters **o**, **oa**, and **ow**.

c**o**ld c**oa**t sn**ow**

Read the words below. Then reread Grow and Glow. Add words from the story to each list.

c**o**ld	c**oa**t	sn**ow**

TEKS 1.3 (A) (2) (v) (7) Decode words in isolation by applying common letter-sound correspondences, including vowel digraphs including ow as in snow.

Name ______________________________

The **long i** vowel sound is spelled with **i, y, igh,** and **ie.**

ch**i**ld fl**y** h**igh** p**ie**

The **long o** vowel sound is spelled with **o, oa, ow,** and **oe.**

c**o**ld c**oa**t sn**ow** d**oe**

The **long e** vowel sound is spelled with **e, ee, ea,** and **ie.**

m**e** t**ee**th s**ea**l p**ie**ce

Read the words. Cut out the words. Sort the words by spelling pattern.

Long i	Long o	Long e

wild	shy	fight	grow
sold	bean	free	shield
he	boat	tie	doe

TEKS 1.3 (A) (2) (i) (ii) (v) Decode words in isolation by applying common letter-sound correspondences, including single letters (consonants and vowels), and vowel digraphs

Name ______________________________

Practice

Phonics: Decoding

The **long i** vowel sound can be spelled with the letters **y**, **igh**, and **ie**.

fl**y** l**igh**t t**ie**

Read each word. Write two more words with the underlined sound-spelling pattern.

tr<u>y</u>	______	______
br<u>igh</u>t	______	______
l<u>ie</u>	______	______

TEKS 1.3 (A) (2) (v) (16) Decode words in isolation by applying common letter-sound correspondences, including vowel digraphs including ie as in pie.

Name ______________________________

The **long i** vowel sound can be spelled with the letters **y**, **igh**, and **ie**.

fl**y** l**igh**t t**ie**

Read the words. Cut out the words. Sort the words by vowel spelling pattern.

shy	cries	high	sigh
tries	fry	fight	sky
pie	might	dry	dries

TEKS **1.3 (A) (2) (v) (16)** Decode words in isolation by applying common letter-sound correspondences, including vowel digraphs including ie as in pie.

Name ____________________

The letters **ie** can stand for the vowel sound in **chief**.
The letters **ie** can also stand for the vowel sound in **pie**.

ch**ie**f p**ie**

Read the words below. Write a rhyming word for each word. Then use two of the words in a sentence.

1. yield ____________________

2. fried ____________________

3. lie ____________________

4. niece ____________________

____

____

Practice

Phonics: Decoding

Name ______________________________

The letters **ie** can stand for the vowel sound in **chief**.
The letters **ie** can also stand for the vowel sound in **pie**.

chi**e**f p**ie**

Read the words. Cut out the words. Sort the words by vowel sound-spelling pattern.

p**ie**	chi**e**f

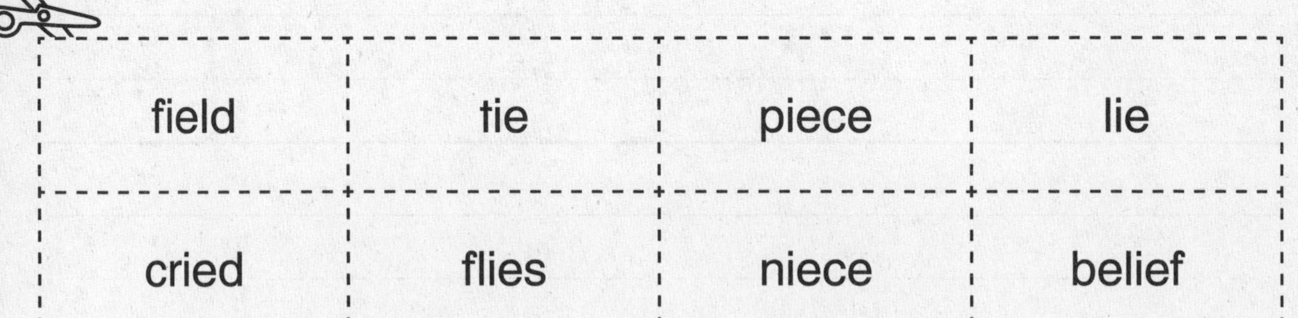

field	tie	piece	lie
cried	flies	niece	belief

TEKS 1.3 (A) (2) (v) (15) (16) Decode words in isolation by applying common letter-sound correspondences including vowel digraphs including ie as in chief and ie as in pie.

Name ______________________________

The consonant digraph **wh** stands for the beginning sound in **wh**ale.

The consonant digraph **ph** stands for the beginning sound in **ph**one.

The consonant digraph **kn** stands for the beginning sound in **kn**ot.

Read each word. Write two more words with the underlined sound-spelling pattern.

<u>wh</u>ich	____________	____________
<u>ph</u>oto	____________	____________
<u>kn</u>ow	____________	____________

TEKS 1.3 (A) (2) (iv) (5) (8) (10) Decode words in isolation by applying common letter-sound correspondences, including consonant digraphs including wh, kn, and ph.

Name ____________________________

The consonant digraph **wh** stands for the beginning sound in **wh**ale.

The consonant digraph **ph** stands for the beginning sound in **ph**one.

The consonant digraph **kn** stands for the beginning sound in **kn**ot.

Read the words. Cut out the words. Sort the words by consonant digraph.

white	graph	know	which
knight	elephant	why	while
photo	knob	wheat	wheel

TEKS 1.3 (A) (2) (iv) (5) (8) (10) Decode words in isolation by applying common letter-sound correspondences, including consonant digraphs including wh, kn, and ph.

Name ____________________

The consonant digraph **wh** stands for the beginning sound in **wh**ale.

The consonant digraph **ph** stands for the beginning sound in **ph**one.

The consonant digraph **kn** stands for the beginning sound in **kn**ot.

Read each word. Write two more words with the underlined sound-spelling pattern.

when	____________	____________
elephant	____________	____________
knock	____________	____________

TEKS 1.3 (A) (2) (iv) (5) (8) (10) Decode words in isolation by applying common letter-sound correspondences, including consonant digraphs including wh, kn, and ph.

Name ____________________

The **long e** vowel sound is also spelled **y** and **ey**.

funn**y** monk**ey**

The **long i** vowel sound is spelled **i**, **y**, **igh**, and **ie**.

ch**i**ld fl**y** h**igh** p**ie**

The **long o** vowel sound is spelled **o**, **oa**, **ow**, and **oe**.

c**o**ld c**oa**t sn**ow** d**oe**

Read the words. Cut out the words. Sort the words by spelling pattern.

Long e	Long i	Long o

sky	key	money	penny
known	so	muddy	might
cries	float	toes	mild

TEKS 1.3 (A) (2) (i) (ii) (iv) Decode words in isolation by applying common letter-sound correspondences, including single letters (consonants and vowels) and consonant digraphs. 1.3 (A) (2) (v) Decode words in isolation by applying common letter-sound correspondences, including vowel digraphs.

Name ______________________________

Practice

Phonics: Decoding

The letters **er**, **ir**, and **ur** stand for the same sounds.

cl**er**k b**ir**ches t**ur**ning

The **long e** vowel sound is also spelled **y** and **ey**.

funn**y** monk**ey**

The **long i** sound is spelled **i**, **y**, **igh**, and **ie**.

ch**i**ld fl**y** h**igh** p**ie**

Read the words. Cut out the words. Sort the words by vowel sound.

Clerk	Key	Child

swirling	finds	jelly	fry
light	alley	bunny	tries
stirring	closer	burning	valley

TEKS **1.3 (C) (1) (vi)** Use common syllabication patterns to decode words, including r-controlled vowel sounds. **1.3 (A) (2) (i) (ii) (v)** Decode words in context and in isolation by applying common letter-sound correspondences, including single letters and vowel digraphs.

Name ______________________________

The letters **ea** can stand for the vowel sound in **heat**.
The letters **ea** can also stand for the vowel sound in **head**.

he**a**t   he**a**d

Read the words. Cut out the words. Sort the words by vowel sound.

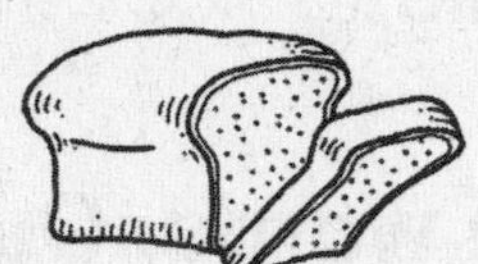

seat	breath	feast	thread
eat	meadow	treat	weather

TEKS 1.3 (A) (2) (v) (3) (4) Decode words in isolation by applying common letter-sound correspondences, including vowel digraphs including ea as in eat and ea as in bread.

Name ________________________________

The letters **ea** can stand for the vowel sound in **heat**.
The letters **ea** can also stand for the vowel sound in **head**.

h**ea**t h**ea**d

Read the words below. Write a rhyming word for each word. Then use two of the words in a sentence.

1. clean ____________________

2. weak ____________________

3. bread ____________________

4. feather ____________________

____

____

TEKS 1.3 (A) (2) (v) (3) (4) Decode words in isolation by applying common letter-sound correspondences, including vowel digraphs including ea as in eat and ea as in bread.

Name ____________________

The letters **ea** can stand for the vowel sound in **heat**.
The letters **ea** can also stand for the vowel sound in **head**.

heat   head

Read each word. Write two more words with the underlined sound-spelling pattern.

m<u>ea</u>n	________	________
tr<u>ea</u>t	________	________
h<u>ea</u>d	________	________
br<u>ea</u>th	________	________

TEKS 1.3 (A) (2) (v) (3) (4) Decode words in isolation by applying common letter-sound correspondences, including vowel digraphs including ea as in eat and ea as in bread.

Name ______________________________

The letters **ou** and **ow** stand for the vowel sound in **mouse** and **clown**.

m**ou**se   cl**ow**n

Read the words below. Write a rhyming word for each word. Then use two of the words in a sentence.

1. cow ______________________________

2. down ______________________________

3. shout ______________________________

4. sound ______________________________

____

____

TEKS **1.3 (A) (2) (v) (6) (8); (vi) (3) (4)** Decode words in isolation by applying common letter-sound correspondences, including vowel digraphs including ow and ou and vowel diphthongs including ou and ow.

Name ____________________

Practice

Phonics: Decoding

The letters **ou** and **ow** stand for the vowel sound in **mouse** and **clown**.

m**ou**se   cl**ow**n

Read the words below. Then reread A Proud Brown Ant. Add words from the story to each list.

m**ou**se	cl**ow**n

TEKS 1.3 (A) (2) (v) (6) (8); (vi) (3) (4) Decode words in isolation by applying common letter-sound correspondences, including vowel digraphs including ow and ou and vowel diphthongs including ou and ow.

Practice

Phonics: Decoding

Name ______________________________

The letters **ow** can stand for the vowel sound in **crown**.
The letters **ow** can also stand for the vowel sound in **snow**.

cr**ow**n   sn**ow**

Read the words below. Write a rhyming word for each word. Then use two of the words in a sentence.

1. show ______________________

2. blown ______________________

3. down ______________________

4. now ______________________

____

____

TEKS 1.3 (A) (2) (v) (6) (7); (vi) (4) Decode words in isolation by applying common letter-sound correspondences, including vowel digraphs including ow and including vowel diphthongs including ow.

Name ______________________________

The letters **ow** can stand for the vowel sound in **crown**.
The letters **ow** can also stand for the vowel sound in **snow**.

cr**ow**n sn**ow**

Read the words. Cut out the words. Sort the words by vowel sound.

how	low	town	glow
down	grow	frown	show

TEKS 1.3 (A) (2) (v) (6) (7); (vi) (4) Decode words in isolation by applying common letter-sound correspondences, including vowel digraphs including ow and including vowel diphthongs including ow.

Practice

Phonics: Decoding

Name ______________________________

The letters **oi** and **oy** stand for the vowel sound in **coins** and **boy**.

co**i**ns boy

Read each word. Write two more words with the same underlined sound-spelling pattern.

joy	______	______
noise	______	______
annoy	______	______
coil	______	______

TEKS 1.3 (A) (2) (vi) (1) (2) Decode words in isolation by applying common letter-sound correspondences, including vowel diphthongs including oy and oi.

Name ____

The letters **oi** and **oy** stand for the vowel sound in **coins** and **boy**.

co**i**ns   bo**y**

Read the words. Cut out the words. Sort the words by vowel spelling pattern.

boil	toy	noise	enjoy
join	soy	spoil	royal

TEKS **1.3 (A) (2) (vi) (1) (2)** Decode words in isolation by applying common letter-sound correspondences, including vowel diphthongs including oy and oi.

Name ____________________

The letters **oi** and **oy** stand for the vowel sound in **coins** and **boy**.

c**oi**ns   b**oy**

Read the words below. Write a rhyming word for each word. Then use two of the words in a sentence.

1. toy ____________________

2. spoil ____________________

3. choice ____________________

4. loyal ____________________

____

____

TEKS 1.3 (A) (2) (vi) (1) (2) Decode words in isolation by applying common letter-sound correspondences, including vowel diphthongs including oy and oi.

Name ______________________________

The letters **oi** and **oy** stand for the vowel sound in **coins** and **boy**.

co**i**ns b**oy**

Read the words below. Then reread Roy's Rich Soil. Add words from the story to each list.

co**i**ns	b**oy**

TEKS 1.3 (A) (2) (vi) (1) (2) Decode words in isolation by applying common letter-sound correspondences, including vowel diphthongs including oy and oi.

Name ______________________________

The letters **ew**, **oo**, and **ou** stand for the vowel sound in **newt**, **moon**, and **soup**.

new**t**   m**oo**n   sou**p**

Read each word. Write two more words with the underlined sound-spelling pattern.

dr<u>ew</u>	____________	____________
st<u>oo</u>l	____________	____________
y<u>ou</u>	____________	____________

TEKS **1.3 (A) (2) (v) (2) (8) (13)** Decode words in isolation by applying common letter-sound correspondences, including vowel digraphs including oo as in moon, ou, and ew.

Name ______________________________

The letters **ew**, **oo**, and **ou** stand for the vowel sound in **newt**, **moon**, and **soup**.

newt　　moon　　soup

Read the words. Cut out the words. Sort the words by vowel sound-spelling pattern.

roof	stew	group	flew
drew	you	tooth	boot
crew	youth	route	soon

TEKS 1.3 (A) (2) (v) (2) (8) (13) Decode words in isolation by applying common letter-sound correspondences, including vowel digraphs including oo as in moon, ou, and ew.

Name ______________________________

The letters **ew**, **oo**, and **ou** stand for the vowel sound in **newt**, **moon**, and **soup**.

newt moon soup

Read the words below. Write a rhyming word for each word. Use two of the words in a sentence.

1. pool ______________________

2. blew ______________________

3. soup ______________________

4. drew ______________________

____

____

TEKS 1.3 (A) (2) (v) (2) (8) (13) Decode words in isolation by applying common letter-sound correspondences, including vowel digraphs including oo as in moon, ou, and ew.

Name ______________________

The letters **ew**, **oo**, and **ou** stand for the vowel sound in **newt**, **moon**, and **soup**.

new**t** m**oo**n s**ou**p

Read each word. Write two more words with the underlined sound-spelling pattern.

sp<u>oo</u>n	______	______
gr<u>ew</u>	______	______
gr<u>ou</u>p	______	______

TEKS **1.3 (A) (2) (v) (2) (8) (13)** Decode words in isolation by applying common letter-sound correspondences, including vowel digraphs including oo as in moon, ou, and ew.

Name ______________________

Practice

Phonics: Decoding

The letters **oo** stand for the vowel sound in **broom**.
The letters **oo** can also stand for the vowel sound in **book.**

br**oo**m b**oo**k

Read the words below. Write a rhyming word for each word. Then use two of the words in a sentence.

1. room ______________________

2. moon ______________________

3. took ______________________

4. wood ______________________

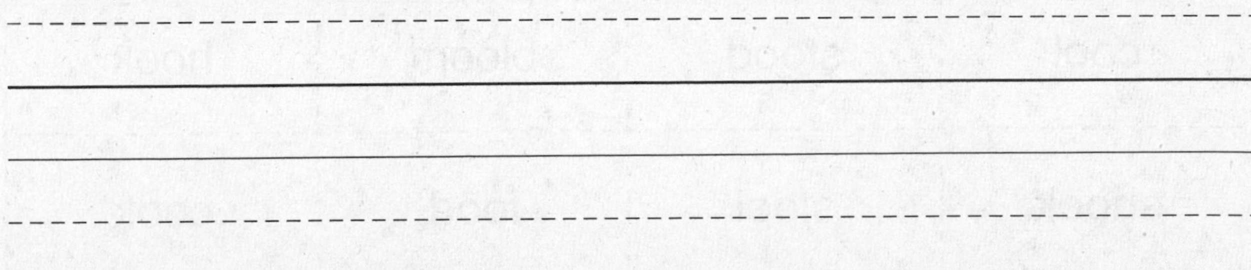

TEKS **1.3 (A) (2) (v) (1) (2)** Decode words in isolation by applying common letter-sound correspondences, including vowel digraphs including oo as in foot and oo as in moon.

Name ______________________________

The letters **oo** stand for the vowel sound in **broom**.
The letters **oo** can also stand for the vowel sound in **book**.

br**oo**m b**oo**k

Read the words. Cut out the words. Sort the words by vowel sound-spelling pattern.

cool	stood	bloom	hook
shook	stool	food	cook

TEKS 1.3 (A) (2) (v) (1) (2) Decode words in isolation by applying common letter-sound correspondences, including vowel digraphs including oo as in foot and oo as in moon.

Name ______________________________

The letters **oo** stand for the vowel sound in **broom**.
The letters **oo** can also stand for the vowel sound in **book**.

br**oo**m b**oo**k

Read each word. Write two more words with the underlined sound-spelling pattern.

pool	______	______
boot	______	______
look	______	______
good	______	______

TEKS 1.3 (A) (2) (v) (1) (2) Decode words in isolation by applying common letter-sound correspondences, including vowel digraphs including oo as in foot and oo as in moon.

Name ____________________

Practice

Phonics: Decoding

The letters **oo** stand for the vowel sound in **broom**.
The letters **oo** can also stand for the vowel sound in **book**.

br**oo**m   b**oo**k

Read the words below. Then reread Let's Find Out. Add words from the story to each list.

br**oo**m	b**oo**k

TEKS 1.3 (A) (2) (v) (1) (2) Decode words in isolation by applying common letter-sound correspondences, including vowel digraphs including oo as in foot and oo as in moon.

Name ______________________________

The letters **ou** can stand for the vowel sound in **mouse**.
The letters **ou** can also stand for the vowel sound in **soup**.

m**ou**se　　　s**ou**p

Read each word. Write two more words with the underlined sound-spelling pattern.

y<u>ou</u>th	______	______
cl<u>ou</u>d	______	______
r<u>ou</u>nd	______	______
gr<u>ou</u>p	______	______

TEKS **1.3 (A) (2) (v) (8); (vi) (3)** Decode words in isolation by applying common letter-sound correspondences, including vowel digraphs including ou and including vowel diphthongs including ou.

Name ______________________________

Practice

Phonics: Decoding

The letters **ou** can stand for the vowel sound in **mouse**.
The letters **ou** can also stand for the vowel sound in **soup**.

m**ou**se s**ou**p

Read the words. Cut out the words. Sort the words by vowel sound-spelling pattern.

house	soup	you	ground
youth	shout	group	proud

TEKS 1.3 (A) (2) (v) (8); (vi) (3) Decode words in isolation by applying common letter-sound correspondences, including vowel digraphs including ou and including vowel diphthongs including ou.

Name ______________________________

The letters **au** and **aw** stand for the vowel sound in **fault** and **paw**.

f**au**lt p**aw**

Read the words below. Write a rhyming word for each word. Then use two of the words in a sentence.

1. vault ______________________

2. pause ______________________

3. gnaw ______________________

4. drawn ______________________

TEKS **1.3 (A) (2) (v) (11) (12)** Decode words in isolation by applying common letter-sound correspondences, including vowel digraphs including aw and au.

Practice

Phonics: Decoding

Name ____________________

The letters **au** and **aw** stand for the vowel sound in **fault** and **paw**.

f**au**lt p**aw**

Read the words. Cut out the words. Sort the words by vowel spelling pattern.

f**au**lt	p**aw**

gnaw	crawling	vault	launch
claw	cause	shawl	faucet

TEKS 1.3 (A) (2) (v) (11) (12) Decode words in isolation by applying common letter-sound correspondences, including vowel digraphs including aw and au.

Name ______________________________

The letters **au** and **aw** stand for the vowel sound in **fault** and **paw**.

f**au**lt　　　p**aw**

Read each word. Write two more words with the underlined sound-spelling pattern.

j<u>aw</u>	________	________
y<u>aw</u>n	________	________
l<u>au</u>nch	________	________
v<u>au</u>lt	________	________

TEKS **1.3 (A) (2) (v) (11) (12)** Decode words in isolation by applying common letter-sound correspondences, including vowel digraphs including aw and au.

Name ______________________________

The letters **au** and **aw** stand for the vowel sound in **fault** and **paw**.

f**au**lt p**aw**

Read the words below. Then reread <u>All for Paul</u>. Add words from the story to each list.

f**au**lt	p**aw**

TEKS 1.3 (A) (2) (v) (11) (12) Decode words in isolation by applying common letter-sound correspondences, including vowel digraphs including aw and au.

Name ______________________________

A B C D E F G H I J K L M N O P Q R S T U V W X Y Z

Use the first letter of a word to put it in ABC order.

Read the words in each line. Write the words in ABC order on the lines below.

1. cat bat hat

2. fit sad must

When the first letters are the same, use the second letter to put the words in ABC order.

Read the words in each line. Write the words in ABC order on the lines below.

3. bat big bug

4. duck dad sun

TEKS **1.6 (E) (1)** Alphabetize a series of words to the first letter.
1.6 (E) (2) Alphabetize a series of words to the second letter.

Name ______________________

A B C D E F G H I J K L M N O P Q R S T U V W X Y Z

Use the first letter of a word to put it in ABC order.

Read the words in each line. Write the words in ABC order on the lines below.

1. ride bike make

2. chess lake time

When the first letters are the same, use the second letter to put the words in ABC order.

Read the words in each line. Write the words in ABC order on the lines below.

3. ran ride rude

4. late time take

TEKS 1.6 (E) (1) Alphabetize a series of words to the first letter.
1.6 (E) (2) Alphabetize a series of words to the second letter.

Name ______________________________

A B C D E F G H I J K L M N O P Q R S T U V W X Y Z

Use the first letter of a word to put it in ABC order.

Read the words in each line. Write the words in ABC order on the lines below.

1. smart far house

2. boy corn storm

When the first letters are the same, use the second letter to put the words in ABC order.

Read the words in each line. Write the words in ABC order on the lines below.

3. barn born black

4. round rest dark

TEKS 1.6 (E) (1) Alphabetize a series of words to the first letter.
1.6 (E) (2) Alphabetize a series of words to the second letter.

Name ______________________________

ABCDEFGHIJKLMNOPQRSTUVWXYZ

Use the first letter of a word to put it in ABC order.

Read the words in each line. Write the words in ABC order on the lines below.

1. apple moon book

2. hen pail walk

When the first letters are the same, use the second letter to put the words in ABC order.

Read the words in each line. Write the words in ABC order on the lines below.

3. picnic past pond

4. safe sun stick

TEKS **1.6 (E) (1)** Alphabetize a series of words to the first letter.
1.6 (E) (2) Alphabetize a series of words to the second letter.